Common Dragonfli
of the Pacific Coast

A Life Size Field Guide

By James S. Walker

Cave Art Press
Anacortes, Washington

ISBN 978-1-934199-26-8

Book design, layout, and editing: Lisa Wright
Cover design: Arlene Cook
Additional editing: Arlene Cook and Réanne Hemingway Douglass
All photographs by James S. Walker, except where credited in text
Original artwork by Sabine Deviche

Cover photo: Paddle-tailed Darner ("Happy-face" Dragonfly)
James S. Walker, Little Cranberry Lake, Anacortes, Washington

Printed and bound in the U.S.A.
First printing: July 2017

Published by Cave Art Press
13589 Clayton Lane
Anacortes WA 98221
www.caveartpress.com

Contents

Dedication

This book is dedicated to my parents, Janet and Ivan Walker,
who were always supportive of my interests and pursuits as a child.

It is also dedicated to my wife Betsy,
my companion in life and nature.

The Dragon-fly

Today I saw the dragon-fly
Come from the wells where he did lie.
An inner impulse rent the veil
Of his old husk: from head to tail
Came out clear plates of sapphire mail.
He dried his wings: like gauze they grew;
Thro' crofts and pastures wet with dew
A living flash of light he flew.

—Alfred, Lord Tennyson (1833)

Preface

People have always been intrigued by dragonflies and damselflies. Their beauty and agile flight catch our attention and beckon us to their world. It's a journey well worth taking.

My connection with dragonflies started when I was five years old. We had moved from the city to a rural area. One brisk autumn morning I was exploring my new backyard when I noticed a huge insect. It was hanging in a low branch of a tree, and its brilliant blue spots and large wings were dazzling in the sun.

I knew it was a dragonfly, from television shows or books I suppose, but I had never seen one in person before. It wasn't moving, even as I approached, so I thought it was dead. I reached out and picked it up ever so gently and rushed inside.

"Look at the dead dragonfly I found," I shouted to my parents in the kitchen.

"Oh, that's nice," they said.

I took my prize to the living room, and hung it on a lampshade—thinking it would add nicely to the décor of the room. A few minutes later I noticed some movement, and suddenly realized that the "dead" dragonfly had warmed up and was very much alive.

Not only was it alive, it was flying vigorously around the room—much to my delight.

"Look. The dragonfly's alive!"

I was enjoying the show, but when my parents came into the room the mood changed suddenly. My Dad grabbed a newspaper, rolled it up, and started to swat at the dragonfly.

"No, no," I protested. "Let it go outside."

I opened the front door, and we cooperated in shooing it in that direction. It quickly took the hint, and fled to its accustomed world of unbounded skies. What a relief—I was afraid my folks were going to kill the poor creature.

Since then, I've continued to be fascinated by dragonflies. I've studied, photographed, led field trips, and given presentations on dragonflies and damselflies (collectively known as odonates) for many years now. This field guide is the culmination of those efforts, and is designed to help interested observers of nature appreciate, identify, and enjoy the most common odonates of the Pacific Coast. I hope you will take this guide with you as you explore your local lakes and ponds, and that it will be your passport to their world!

Introduction

This book is designed to help you appreciate the wonder, beauty, and drama of dragonflies and their close relatives, the damselflies. All you need to get started is a pair of binoculars and a point-and-shoot camera. Any nearby pond, lake, marsh, or wetland will do just fine as a dragonflying location.

Dragonflies and damselflies are beautiful creatures, with colors and patterns that rival those of any bird or butterfly. As with other insect species, some of the basic facts about them may seem surprising:

- They have excellent vision, but can't hear.
- They have six legs, but don't walk.
- They are fierce predators of other insects, but are harmless to humans.
- They are found in the geological record for over 300 million years, and are still going strong today (figure 1).

This field guide contains descriptions and photographs of sixty of the most common species of dragonflies and damselflies found along the Pacific Coast of the United States and Canada. They are presented in taxonomic order; that is, with closely related species grouped together. Each species is described on its own two-page spread that includes a range map, flight-season chart, and a life-size photograph.

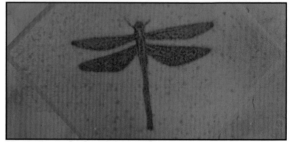

Fig. 1. Cast of a fossil dragonfly.

Fantastic Beasts: Dragonflies, Damselflies, and People

In Western and European cultures, dragonflies are traditionally seen as evil, sometimes even as forms taken by the devil (or drac, as in dracula). The "drac-fly" or "dragonfly" carries that heritage in its name. All sorts of folklore surround dragonflies, including the belief that they can sew up the mouth or toes of sleeping people, or that they are able to insert their long abdomens in the human ear, and penetrate into the brain. One of their common nicknames is "the devil's darning needle"—which is why one family of dragonfly is named the darner.

The truth is that dragonflies are completely harmless to humans. They don't bite people, and their long wasp-like abdomens hold no danger—dragonflies have no sting and no venom. Dragonflies have no interest in humans; they focus their attention on capturing and eating mosquitos, houseflies, and other flying insects.

Other cultures see dragonflies in a much more favorable light. Native Americans consider dragonflies to be beautiful symbols of nature, and they associate the different colors of dragonflies with different seasons of their crops. Asian cultures also have positive feelings for dragonflies. The Japanese interpret dragonflies as symbols of luck, strength, and prosperity. They may even adorn samurai helmets and swords with images of dragonflies, and they write beautiful dragonfly-related haiku, such as:

> Red dragonfly on my shoulder,
> Calls me his friend.
> Autumn has arrived.

There actually is a red dragonfly in our range that lands on people in the fall—its name is the Autumn Meadowhawk (figure 2).

Fig. 2. Autumn Meadowhawks are friendly insects—they will land on your shoulder, your hat, basically any place that has good exposure to the sun.

Dragonflies versus Damselflies

Dragonflies and damselflies are both members of the order of insects known as Odonata—literally, toothed jaws—a reference to their powerful "tooth-like" mouth parts. Collectively, they are referred to as odonates.

Dragonflies are in the suborder anisoptera, pronounced "an-eye-**sop**-ter-a." The literal meaning of anispotera is "an (not)—iso (equal)—ptera (wings)," which refers to the fact that the forewings and hindwings are different. The forewings can be only so wide without hitting the hindwings, but the hindwings can be much wider, depending on the flight characteristics of a particular species.

The main feature that distinguishes dragonflies from damselflies is that dragonflies are stocky, robust insects who hold their wings straight out or forward when perched. In addition, their large compound eyes occupy almost the entire head, and usually meet in the middle. Their flight is strong, fast, and purposeful—dragonflies know where they're going, and they get there fast.

In contrast, damselflies are small, delicate insects, with thin bodies and small well-separated eyes. They belong to the suborder zygoptera (zy-**gop**-ter-a), which means "paired wings." When damselflies perch, they fold their wings along the body—except for spreadwing damselflies, who hold their wings out at about 45 degrees to the body. Their flight is basically a slow, drifting hover as they move through dense shoreline vegetation (figure 3).

Fig. 3. Dragonflies are large, sturdy insects that generally hold their wings straight out when perched. Damselflies are much smaller and lighter, but they don't shy away from harassing dragonflies that venture into their territory. In this case, a Northern/Boreal Bluet is letting a California Darner know it's not welcome.

Eat · Prey · Love:
The Lives of Dragonflies and Damselflies

Eggs and Larvae

All dragonflies and damselflies start their lives as eggs. These are generally small, yellow, rice-sized or smaller, and are deposited either directly into water or placed in shoreline or submergent vegetation. In some species, a female produces small masses of eggs at the tip of her abdomen, which she drops into open water—always trying to avoid fish on the lookout for a quick snack. In other species, females drop one or a few eggs at a time onto floating algae or along a damp shoreline. Damselflies, and the family of dragonflies known as darners, cut slits in the stems of vegetation or in floating logs, and deposit a few eggs in each slit.

Once the eggs hatch, typically within a couple weeks of being laid, the larval stage of the odonate's life begins. Damselfly larvae are long and thin, with external gills extending from the tip of the abdomen—almost like the tail fins of a fish (figure 4a).

Fig. 4a. Damselfly larvae are thin and delicate. The dark "blades" extending from the tip of the abdomen are gills.

Fig. 4b. Dragonfly larvae are stocky. Their gills are out of view, inside the abdomen.

They swim by undulating their bodies in a snake-like or fish-like motion. In contrast, dragonfly larvae are stocky and robust, with internal gills tucked inside their abdomens (figure 4b). They can crawl along the bottom or shoot forward rapidly, propelled by a burst of water expelled from the tip of the abdomen. In both damselflies and dragonflies, small backpack-like "wing buds" extend backwards from the thorax.

Odonata larvae are ferocious predators in their underwater world. Dragonfly larvae, in particular, are known to stalk and attack a variety of prey, ranging from mosquito larvae to tadpoles, from newts to small fish. The larvae shed their skin and increase in size as they mature, eventually reaching the size where they emerge from the water, dry out, and split the skin to allow the adult winged insect to emerge (figure 5). After this, no further shedding of skin occurs, and the odonate has reached its final size.

Emerging adults spend an hour or so expanding their wings and allowing them to dry and harden

Fig. 5. The shed larval skin (exuvia) of a dragonfly.

before taking wing. A freshly-emerged dragonfly or damselfly is referred to as a *teneral* (figure 6). At this stage, their wings are soft and pliable, like cellophane, and their colors are pale and translucent. Teneral odonates can barely fly and are vulnerable to predation.

Fig. 6. A newly emerged (teneral) Common Green Darner. Note the pale colors and fragile wings.

Odonates live the rest of their lives as aerial creatures, with impressive flight skills. They can flap each of their four wings independently, allowing them to fly forward, hover, turn on a dime, and even fly backward. Their legs, which sport impressive side bristles, are used for perching and for capturing prey in midair. The four rear legs form a nice "basket" for sweeping up the prey, and the front two legs are used to process the catch. The front two legs of dragonflies are often tucked up behind the head when perched, and even in flight—until a capture is made.

Mating

When adult odonates mate they first attach "in tandem," with the tip of the male's abdomen attached to the back of the head of the female in dragonflies, or to the front of the thorax in damselflies. They may spend considerable time flying together in tandem before they continue with the mating process. Mating

Fig. 8. Common Green Darners illustrate the wheel position in dragonflies. The tip of the male's abdomen is attached to the back of the female's head, and the tip of the female's abdomen is attached to segment 2 of the male's abdomen.

occurs in the "wheel position," in which the tip of the female's abdomen is brought into contact with the base of the male's abdomen (figures 7 and 8). The wheel position is unique to odonates—no other animal in the world uses it—and *all* odonates mate this way.

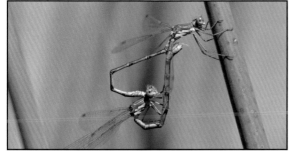

Fig. 7. Spotted Spreadwing damselflies illustrate the wheel position. The tip of the male's abdomen is attached to the front of the female's thorax. The tip of the female's abdomen is attached to segment 2 of the male's abdomen.

Now here's the key part of the mating process: During mating the male removes sperm from previous males and replaces it with his own. As a result, he now has an investment in the female, who will be laying eggs fertilized with his sperm. This leads to various types of "guarding behavior," in which a male protects *his* female from further matings as she lays his eggs. Guarding is often accomplished by the male remaining in tandem as the female lays eggs. In other cases, where the male's abdomen is inflexible and remaining in tandem is difficult, the male may hover over the female as she dips and lays eggs in the water.

Life Span and Flight Season

Most of the odonates in our range have a life span of roughly one year. They are laid as eggs in mid to late summer, they hatch in the water in the fall, overwinter underwater, and then emerge as adults the following spring or early summer. They spend the few short months of their adult lives eating, defending territory, and reproducing, finally dying of exhaustion late in the summer.

In exceptional cases their lives may be a bit longer. The Black Petaltail, for example, breeds at high elevation where the growing season for its larvae is short. As a result, it may take five or more years for the larvae to mature enough to emerge as an adult. Other notable exceptions are migratory species, like the Common Green Darner and the Variegated Meadowhawk. In these species there is evidence that adults fly south in the fall, overwinter in Southern California or Mexico, and then migrate back north in early spring. Their total life span is probably a year and a half to two years, though little is known yet about this aspect of dragonfly biology.

The time during which the adult odonate is active is referred to as its *flight season*. Each species in this guide has a two-page spread that includes a flight-season chart, showing the percentage of observations of that species for each month of the year. Some species peak early in the season, some mid season, and others fly late into the fall—sometimes until frost brings their season to an end. Other species have spent their lives by mid summer, and are gone long before the weather turns cold (figure 9).

Paying attention to the flight season charts may help you distinguish between similar dragonfly or damselfly species.

Habitats

All odonates spend the early part of their lives in fresh water. Adults are generally found in various freshwater habitats—wetlands, marshes, ponds, lakes, rivers. They prefer water features with lots of shoreline vegetation, where they can perch to hunt, mate, and emerge from their larval skins.

Sometimes overlooked, but also good habitats for dragonflies and damselflies, are ditches and temporary ponds. It's not uncommon to see dragonflies laying eggs in areas that are dry in the summer, when the eggs are deposited, but which will be flooded with water in the fall. Damselflies also lay eggs in the stems of vegetation in areas like this.

Predators

Dragonflies are top predators in their insect world, but many other animals feed on them. Foremost among the dragonfly predators are birds, which are very efficient hunters. Merlins and American Kestrels, in particular, are known to have a penchant for dragonflies, usually large darners, sometimes picking off a couple at a time. Even so, dragonflies and damselflies reproduce in such numbers that they can withstand the onslaught.

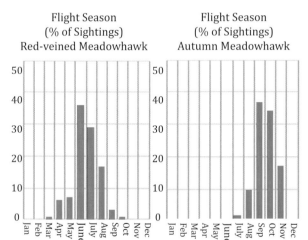

Fig. 9. Flight Season chart for the Red-veined Meadowhawk (left), and the Autumn Meadowhawk (right).

The Anatomy of Dragonflies and Damselflies

The basic anatomical features of dragonflies and damselflies are illustrated in figures 10 a-c.

Head

The head is the smallest section of the body, and is almost hollow in back—especially in dragonflies. This allows it great freedom to swivel and pivot as the odonate tracks prey. The compound eyes occupy a large portion of the head, and generally meet in the middle in dragonflies.

Thorax

The thorax is the power center of the body. It contains the flight muscles that control the four wings, and is also the attachment point for the six legs. The thorax often has stripes on the front and sides that are key field marks.

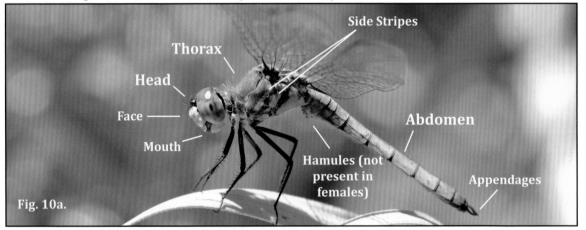

Fig. 10a.

Thorax · Head · Face · Mouth · Side Stripes · Abdomen · Hamules (not present in females) · Appendages

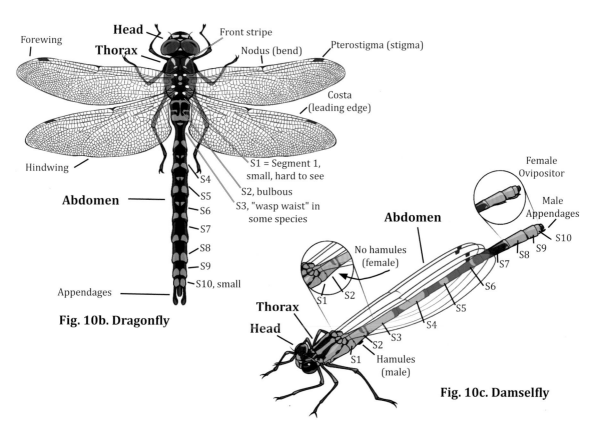

Head

Forewing

Thorax

Front stripe

Nodus (bend)

Pterostigma (stigma)

Costa (leading edge)

Hindwing

S1 = Segment 1, small, hard to see

S2, bulbous

S3, "wasp waist" in some species

S4

Abdomen

S5

S6

S7

S8

S9

Appendages

S10, small

Fig. 10b. Dragonfly

Female Ovipositor

Male Appendages

Abdomen

No hamules (female)

S1

S2

S10

S9

S8

S7

S6

S5

S4

S3

Thorax

S2

Head

S1   Hamules (male)

Fig. 10c. Damselfly

Fig. 11. Hamules are the prominent structures on the underside of segment 2 of the male's abdomen. They serve as "latches" to hold the male and female together in the wheel position.

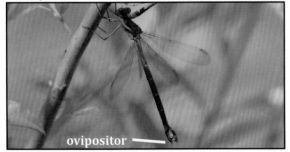

Fig. 12. The ovipositor, or egg-laying structure, can be seen as an expanded tip on the female's abdomen. The small projections are used to probe for a suitable place to deposit eggs.

Abdomen

The abdomen, in addition to being the location for food digestion, produces sperm in males and eggs in females. It also plays a key role in attaching males and females in tandem, as well as in the wheel position. The abdomen consists of ten segments, counting from number one (abbreviated S1) nearest to the thorax, to number ten (S10) at the tip of the abdomen. Under S2 in male odonates are the *hamules* (figure 11), a paired structure that attaches the abdomen of the male to the tip of the female's abdomen during mating. The underside of S2 in females is smooth and flat.

In some species, the tip of the female's abdomen contains an *ovipositor*. This is the structure that cuts slits in stems and deposits eggs inside. The ovipositor can be seen as an expanded area near the tip of the abdomen (figure 12), with some small projections visible on the underside.

Other species develop a wax-like coating on the abdomen that gives it a bright blue or white color (figure 13). This is referred to as *pruinosity*, because it is similar to the light-colored "bloom" that forms on the surface of a prune (figure 14). In some cases, the grip of the female

Fig. 13. The abdomen of the Common Whitetail displays pruinosity.

during mating rubs the pruinosity off in the middle of the abdomen, exposing the darker abdominal surface lying under the pruinose coating (figure 15).

Fig 15. The dark area in the middle of the male Eight-spotted Skimmer's abdomen shows where pruinosity has been rubbed off by the female while in the wheel position.

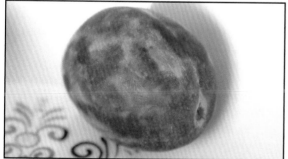

Fig. 14. The bluish "bloom" of pruinosity on the surface of a plum.

Appendages

Among the distinctive features of dragonfly and damselfly anatomy are the projections found at the tip of the abdomen. These are referred to as appendages, and all dragonflies and damselflies have them. They are most important in males, because they are used to attach the abdomen of the male to the body of the female. Females may also use them to feel around during attachment in the wheel position, or during egg laying.

Male dragonflies have three appendages—two above, and one below. The upper appendages are called *cerci*, and the lower appendage is the *epiproct*. When a male grasps a female with his abdomen, the two cerci wrap around behind the head of the female and attach in its hollow backside. The exact shape of the cerci is important, as they attach to the female in a lock-and-key fashion, ensuring that mating is usually between individuals of the same species. The epiproct grips the front of the female's head, between the eyes.

Female dragonflies lack an epiproct. In some species, the tip of the abdomen is enlarged to contain an ovipositor that cuts slits in vegetation for deposition of the eggs. In others, the abdomen has a funnel-shaped *egg scoop* on the underside near the tip, from which eggs are released.

In damselflies, the male has four appendages—two above and two below. The upper appendages are again referred to as cerci, but the two lower appendages are called *paraprocts*. The male uses these appendages to attach to the front of the female's thorax. Females have reduced cerci, but no paraprocts. Instead of paraprocts, they have a prominent ovipositor for egg laying.

Wings

All dragonflies and damselflies have four wings. The leading edge of a wing is referred to as the *costa*, the bend in the leading edge is the *nodus*, and the dark mark near the tip is the *pterostigma*—or simply stigma for short. Stigmas add a bit of weight to the wing tips, making for a more efficient connection between the flight muscles and the wings.

Though many species have clear wings, there are a number that are distinguished by the various types of markings in their wings. Some species have a dark or colored "patch" near the base of the wing;

some have dark patches or spots farther out in the wing; some have pruinose white spots or patches in the wings (figures 16 a-d).

Fig. 16a.

Fig. 16b.

a) Four-spotted Skimmer
c) River Jewelwing

b) Flame Skimmer
d) Twelve-spotted Skimmer

Fig. 16c.

Fig. 16d.

Dragonfly and Damselfly Vision

Dragonflies and damselflies are noted for their incredible vision. They have compound eyes, which are composed of thousands of individual eyes (figure 17a). Each of these small eyes is called an *ommatidium*. A typical compound eye has roughly 30,000 ommatidia packed together in a hexagonal pattern.

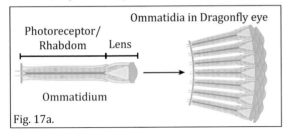

Ommatidia in Dragonfly eye

Photoreceptor/ Rhabdom   Lens

Ommatidium

Fig. 17a.

An ommatidium can be thought of as an independent eye, with a lens collecting and focusing light coming into it from the direction in which it points. Each one produces an image of a small part of the odonate's visual field. Collectively, they work like the pixels of a TV screen; each pixel represents just a small part of the total picture, but when blended together they give a complete view.

Pseudopupils

When you look at the compound eye of a dragonfly, you may notice a dark spot in your line of sight—the dragonfly appears to be looking back at you. The dark spot looks like the pupil of a vertebrate's eye, but there *is* no pupil in an insect eye. Because of its similar appearance, however, it's referred to as a *pseudopupil*. The pseudopupil is formed when your line of sight goes to the base of an ommatidium (figure 17b). It looks dark because that's where the light-absorbing component—the *rhabdom*—is located.

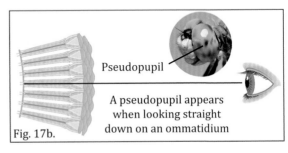

Pseudopupil

A pseudopupil appears when looking straight down on an ommatidium

Fig. 17b.

The pseudopupil doesn't act like a typical vertebrate pupil, however. If you move around, you find that the pseudopupil follows your motion (figure 17c). It can give you a creepy feeling, until you realize the dragonfly is seeing in all of those directions at the same time, regardless of your current position.

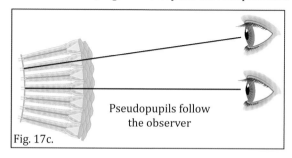

Pseudopupils follow the observer

Fig. 17c.

Secondary and Higher-Order Pseudopupils

When you look more carefully at a dragonfly eye, you'll often notice that it has additional dark spots. In fact, the primary pseudopupil along your line of sight is surrounded by a group of secondary pseudopupils. Even fainter higher-order pseudopupils are seen farther away from the primary pseudopupil.

These secondary and higher-order pseudopupils are the result of total internal reflections within an ommatidium. Imagine looking in a direction away from the primary pseudopupil (figure 17d). If you're looking at just the right angle, your line of sight shows a reflected image of the dark base of a different ommatidium. This produces a fainter secondary pseudopupil some distance away from the primary pseudopupil. More internal reflections produce even higher-order pseudopupils.

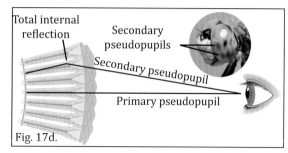

Total internal reflection

Secondary pseudopupils

Secondary pseudopupil

Primary pseudopupil

Fig. 17d.

Dorsal Fovea and Giant Pseudopupils

Another interesting feature of the dragonfly eye is the *dorsal fovea*. It's called this because it's located on the top of the eye (the dorsal surface), and is the area of the eye with the sharpest vision (as in a mammalian fovea). The dorsal fovea is often a different color from the rest of the eye (figure 18). Thus, several species are described as having eyes that are, for example, red above (on the dorsal fovea) and yellowish below.

As a result, when you look straight down on the dorsal fovea of a dragonfly, you see large pseudopupils looking back at you (figure 19). When a dragonfly wants a particularly sharp view of a passing insect, it pivots its head to point the dorsal fovea of its eyes at the target.

Fig. 18. Dorsal fovea (red) on a Striped Meadowhawk.

The ommatidia in the dorsal fovea point primarily in one direction. This results in a large number of "pixels," and an enhanced resolution in that direction.

Fig. 19. The individual eyes (ommatidia) in the dorsal fovea of a Blue Dasher form exceptionally large black spots, the pseudopupils, when looking straight down on the dorsal fovea.

White Spots on the Eyes

When observing dragonfly eyes on a bright sunny day, it's common to see prominent white spots on them (figures 20 and 21). These are reflections of the sun, not actual spots on the eyes themselves. It's not surprising that such reflections exist, given that the surface of a compound eye is fairly smooth and shiny, like a football helmet. If you look carefully, though, you'll notice that the white spots are actually hexagonal in shape, not circular. This is due to diffraction effects from the hexagonal arrangement of ommatidia on the eye's surface.

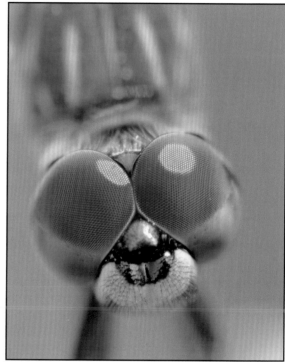

Fig. 20. The white spot on this Blue Dasher's eye is a reflection of the sun. Its six-sided shape is due to the hexagonal arrangement of the ommatidia.

Fig. 21. The white spots on the red dorsal fovea of this female Blue Dasher's eyes are reflections of the sun. The granularity of individual ommatidia is visible.

Egg Laying in Damselflies and Dragonflies

One of the most varied behaviors of dragonflies and damselflies is the way in which they lay eggs (figure 22). In some species, the tip of the female's abdomen is dipped gently into the water as a pair hovers together in tandem. In others, the male hovers overhead as the female dips in the water by herself. Still others remain in tandem as the female cuts slits in vegetation with her ovipositor and lays eggs inside. Even more possibilities are presented below.

Egg Laying in Damselflies

A number of damselflies, and especially bluets, lay their eggs by submerging themselves underwater. This might seem odd, since the adults are air-breathing animals. However, a thin coating of air clings to their bodies as they descend, and they can spend as much as an hour underwater before they need to resurface.

The process begins with a male and female in tandem landing on a small stem of vegetation extending out of the water. The pair then backs down the stem, with the female in the lead. When the pair is deep enough that the male is submerged up to his thorax he usually detaches and hovers above the water waiting for his mate to resurface.

Once the female is completely submerged she cuts slits in the stem and lays eggs inside. During this process she remains safe from males in the air who would like to grab her to attempt mating. When she finishes laying eggs, you might expect her simply to climb back up the stem until she resurfaces. Instead, she simply lets go and slowly floats to the surface. She then breaks through, begins to beat her wings and, as the male reattaches, flies off in tandem again to repeat the process elsewhere.

Egg Laying in Black Saddlebags

Black Saddlebags, and other saddlebag species as well, have their own unique way of laying eggs. They begin by hovering in tandem for some time over a promising patch of open water. They are concerned about fish who would like to eat their eggs, or even make a grab for the adults themselves, so they take their time making sure the coast is clear.

When the male is satisfied, he rapidly dips his hindwings as a signal to the female, and then releases his grip on her. She descends to the water's surface, taps it with her abdomen to release a few eggs, and then ascends. As she starts upward the male descends and rejoins her in mid-air, where he reattaches and flies off with her to scout another area.

Fig. 22. Autumn Meadowhawks in tandem. The female has picked up a water droplet with her egg scoop and is laying eggs in it. (See next page for further discussion.)

Egg Laying in Autumn Meadowhawks

The egg-laying procedure in Autumn Meadowhawks involves repeatedly smashing the female into shoreline vegetation. This sounds crazy, but it makes sense for Autumn Meadowhawks (Fig. 23). Their four-step, egg-laying process is shown in a series of illustrations in figures 24 a-d.

Close-up of egg scoop

b.

a.

Fig. 23 a-b. The female Autumn Meadowhawk (a) is noted for its large egg scoop (b). Its purpose is to hold a drop of water during the egg-laying process.

Step 1 (a): The pair hovers in tandem until the female is ready to proceed.

Step 2 (b): The pair dips down so that the tip of the female's abdomen is in the water. She doesn't lay eggs just yet, as many species do, but simply collects a droplet of water. The droplet is held in place by the large egg scoop of the female.

Step 3 (c): The pair hovers for a couple seconds as the female lays eggs into the droplet of water. The droplet goes from being transparent to noticeably yellow during this process.

Step 4 (d): The pair swoops downward rapidly, violently whacking the female's abdomen against a stem of shoreline vegetation to dislodge the egg-bearing droplet.

Check damp shoreline vegetation late in the year to see this behavior. In some cases, small groups of Autumn Meadowhawk pairs will be seen laying eggs together.

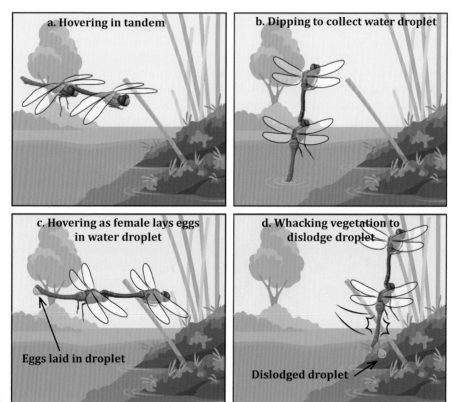

a. Hovering in tandem

b. Dipping to collect water droplet

c. Hovering as female lays eggs in water droplet

Eggs laid in droplet

d. Whacking vegetation to dislodge droplet

Dislodged droplet

Fig. 24 a-d.

Splash-Dunk / Spin-Dry Behavior

Dragonflies like to keep themselves clean. Whenever a dragonfly perches it immediately begins to clean its eyes. It would like to clean its wings and abdomen as well, since these also accumulate various types of debris, but it can't because the wings stick straight out from the body and the abdomen is very long. About the only way a dragonfly can clean these body parts is to plunge into the water—that is, to do a splash-dunk followed by a spin-dry (figures 25 and 26).

To be specific, a dragonfly does a splash-dunk by plowing head first into the water at full speed. When it hits, it sends up a sizeable splash and comes to a complete stop. After being immersed in the water for about half a second, the dragonfly takes wing again. It typically does a few splash-dunks in a row, up to a record number of eight.

Fig. 25. Spinning dragonfly (1,000 rpm).

The splash-dunk is only half of the process. After the splash-dunks, the dragonfly needs to shed the water it has picked up. I was fortunate enough to discover their method of drying off a few years ago—they gain altitude, and then tumble head over heels in a motion I call a spin-dry. The dragonflies spin at 1,000 rpm during the spin-dry—the fastest known spinning motion of any animal—and water shoots out in all directions, giving a nice show.

Please note that spinning at 1,000 rpm does not mean the dragonfly spins 1,000 times, or that it spins for a minute—it simply means that the *rate* of spinning is such that if a dragonfly were to spin for a minute it would complete 1,000 revolutions. In fact, a typical spin-dry consists of about six revolutions in just under half a second. The centripetal acceleration produced by the spin is roughly 25 times the acceleration due to gravity, more than enough to shed the water.

Though a number of species have been observed to splash-dunk and spin-dry—including several species of darners, skimmers, and meadowhawks—the undisputed champion of this behavior is the Paddle-tailed Darner. To observe it, look for darners flying low over the water late in the year. If you see one perform a splash-dunk, keep watching. It may do a couple more splash-dunks, but when it begins to fly straight upward you'll know it's getting ready to do a spin-dry. When the lighting is favorable, the spin-dry will be visible mainly by the water droplets that shoot outward.

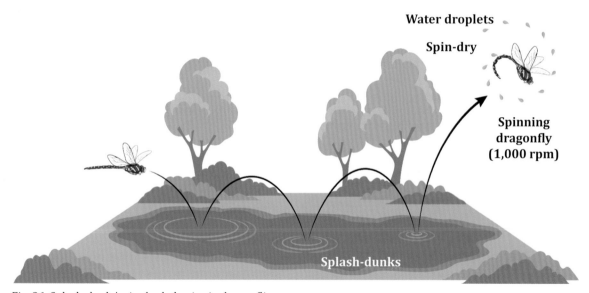

Fig. 26. Splash-dunk/spin-dry behavior in dragonflies.

How to Train Your Dragonfly: The Fine Art of Dragonfly Whispering

Dragonflies are easier to interact with than you might think. If you see one perched (figure 27), try sliding your finger up the stem until you're touching its rear legs. At that point give it a little "tickle," and it will often transfer its legs from the stem to your finger (figure 28). When that happens you have "whispered" the dragonfly.

Fig. 28. A "whispered" dragonfly considers your finger its new perch.

Once a dragonfly is on your finger, it's likely to stay there for a long period of time. You can walk around with it, show it to other people, take pictures of it, and so on. You can even transfer it to another person (figure 29). If you see another dragonfly in the bushes, you might "whisper" that one as well; you just might find yourself with a "fist full of dragons" (figure 30).

Some dragonflies don't need to be "whispered"—they'll come to you. Just stand still in a sunny spot in autumn, and chances are a small red dragonfly—an Autumn Meadowhawk—will join you. Usually only one or two will land on you at a time, but sometimes they can be quite numerous (figure 31).

Fig. 27. A perching dragonfly waiting to be "whispered."

Fig. 29. A whispered dragonfly can be transferred to another person.

Fig. 30. Once a dragonfly has been whispered onto a finger, it will generally stay there as you whisper others.

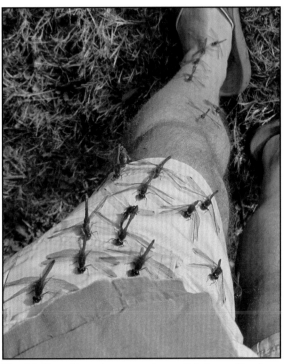

Fig. 31. Sometimes large numbers of Autumn Meadowhawks emerge at nearly the same time. In such cases, you may find yourself covered in dragonflies.

Tips for Observing and Photographing Odonates

The first step in observing dragonflies and damselflies is to find them in their natural habitat. This means looking for a freshwater feature of some kind in your neighborhood—perhaps a lake, a pond, a marsh, or even a ditch. The water should be warm and fairly calm, since wave action can make it hard for larvae to thrive. This rules out large bodies of water and fast running mountain streams. Also look for water with lots of shoreline vegetation where odonates like to perch and emerge from their larval skin.

Finding Perched Dragonflies

Dragonflies and damselflies can often be observed on the wing, but the best situation is to find one that's perched. Now you can look at it in detail with your binoculars, and practice looking for and recognizing the field marks that are used for identification.

To find perched odonates, look for bushes and other vegetation in full sunshine some distance back from the shore. Scan the vegetation for streaks of blue or red color coming from their bodies. You might also find one by spotting the shimmering light that glints from its wings. Approach the bushes step by step, getting progressively better views. If a dragonfly or a damselfly flushes before you get a chance to see it perched don't worry— it's a good sign that others are perching in the same general area. Sometimes you'll see one fly by rather slowly; keep watching because it just might land.

Observing Odonates with Binoculars

Binoculars allow you to see every detail of the odonate's body, from the colorful spots and stripes on its body, to the intricate cells of its wings. It can be tricky at first, however, to get an odonate into the field of view of your binoculars. A good way to start is to look for something prominent near your odonate. Let's say a dragonfly you want to examine is above and to the right of a bright yellow leaf. The leaf is larger and brighter than the dragonfly, so look for it first—it should be relatively easy to find with your binoculars. Once you have the leaf in the field of view, just pan up and to the right, in the two o'clock direction, to find the dragonfly. The same procedure applies to observing dragonflies with spotting scopes, which provide even more incredible close-up views than binoculars.

Almost any pair of binoculars will work fine for dragonflying. Many people use binoculars that are rated 8 x 32. The magnification is 8 times actual size, while the diameter of the main lens is 32 mm. Binoculars with magnifications in the range of 7 to 10 will work nicely, though 10 power binoculars have a relatively small field of view and can be hard to hold steady. The size of the main lens is generally in the range of 25 mm to 40 mm, with 32 mm a nice intermediate size. The main criterion in choosing binoculars is to find a pair that feels comfortable in your hands, and isn't too heavy to hang around your neck for extended periods of time. Binoculars with close-focusing ability are also a plus.

Many dragonfly field trips involve someone swinging a net at every dragonfly they see. This all too often results in injured or dead dragonflies—even dragonfly experts occasionally behead dragonflies with their nets. It just doesn't make sense to harm the creatures we want to admire. Nets should be used only for valid scientific research, not for the purposes of show and tell.

If you patiently look for perched dragonflies, observe them with your binoculars, and take pictures of them with your camera, you will find that dragonflying is an enriching and rewarding experience—and you'll have the great satisfaction of knowing that no dragonflies have been harmed.

Photographing Dragonflies and Damselflies

Today's cameras are great! They're easy to use, produce wonderful pictures, and you can take all the shots you want—you can always delete some later. Many of the photos in this guide were taken with a basic point-and-shoot camera. The majority of the photos, however, were taken with a Nikon DSLR and a 105 mm macro lens. This lens takes exceptionally sharp pictures, but you have to get fairly close to your subject. (This shouldn't be a problem, though, once you're good at dragonfly whispering!) For longer-range shots you might try a Canon DSLR with a 180 mm macro lens. It has longer reach, but generally requires a tripod for best results.

Once you see a perched dragonfly or damselfly, start by taking a couple pictures of it. Now take a step or two towards it and take another couple pictures. Keep repeating this process, and soon you'll find yourself right up next to your target. If the dragonfly takes off, don't take it personally—it probably left for its own reasons, like chasing prey or pursuing a potential mate. Sometimes you're ready to snap a great picture when the odonate flies off. Don't worry. Often it will land again in the same general area—and sometimes in a position that's even better for a picture than before!

One problem that comes up frequently is that your camera will focus on objects in the background rather than on the dragonfly in the foreground. Here's a good way to get around this problem. First, look for something prominent (like a flower or rock) that's *closer* to you than the dragonfly. Focus on this object, and then point the camera back toward the dragonfly. The dragonfly is now out of focus, because you're focused at a shorter distance. Press the shutter halfway down and the autofocus will start moving outward as it tries to focus. When it hits the dragonfly it stops, and gives a sharp focus, with the background still out of focus. This will give you a sharply focused dragonfly with a pleasing, uniformly-colored background (figure 32).

Fig. 32. Focusing on a nearby dragonfly, with vegetation far in the background, results in a photo with a pleasing and non-distracting background.

Tips for Identifying Dragonflies and Damselflies

It's fun to watch dragonflies and enjoy their beautiful colors, but it's even more fun to watch them when you actually "know them by name." This section presents some of the basic questions you should ask yourself as you go through the process of identifying an odonate. The answers will narrow down your choices to a few different species, or even just one.

DRAGONFLY OR DAMSELFLY? The first question is one of the easiest—is the odonate you're looking at a dragonfly or a damselfly? Dragonflies are larger and stockier than damselflies, with large prominent eyes that occupy most of the head. They fly energetically and with purpose, and perch with their wings held straight out, or angled forward. Damselflies are thin and delicate. Their flight is a gentle hover, and they fold their wings when perched, or hold them back at 45 degrees. Damselfly eyes are small and well separated. After you see a few species of dragonflies and damselflies, the differences will be readily apparent.

MALE OR FEMALE? It's useful to know if the odonate you're looking at is a male or a female. In some species the sexes are quite different, and the males change their appearance from "female-like" to "male-like" as they mature. Even so, males can always be identified by the presence of hamules under segment 2 of the abdomen, and by their relatively larger appendages. In contrast, females either have an egg scoop on the underside of the abdomen, or a prominent ovipositor. Females generally have cryptic coloration that gives them camouflage when they spend time away from the water feeding and resting.

Fig. 33. A Variable Darner (left) shares a sunny perch with a Striped Meadowhawk (right).

PERCHER OR FLYER? Another way to narrow down which species of dragonfly you're looking at is to determine whether it is a percher or a flyer. Perchers rest horizontally, and take off and return to their perches time and again. The most common perchers are skimmers and meadowhawks. Flyers hang vertically when perched, like a Christmas ornament. When they leave their perch they are gone—don't wait for them to return. Darners are the most prominent flyers.

WHICH FAMILY? With some practice you'll begin to recognize the different families of dragonflies and damselflies. Darners have long, thin abdomens; skimmers are stocky and often have colorful wings; meadowhawks are red and fairly small; bluets are mostly blue; spreadwings are long and thin and hold their wings out at 45 degrees when perched. Recognizing the families will quickly narrow down the identification.

WHICH SPECIES? Check the field marks that are pointed out in each species description to make your final identification. Try to verify as many different field marks as possible; the more field marks that agree with a certain species the more confident you can be of your identification.

Age-related Differences

As odonates age, their appearance can change significantly. In general, colors tend to darken with age. Young odonates have light, vibrant (plastic-like) colors to go with their glossy wings. With age the colors darken and deepen in shade. Sometimes older individuals can become so dark that it can be hard to distinguish the field marks. The wings also become scuffed with age, and often show tears and rips.

One of the most striking changes with age is the appearance of the side stripes on the thorax of certain species. For example, the Cardinal Meadowhawk has white side stripes when young. As individuals of this species age, the stripes fade and get darker until only white spots at the base of the stripes remain. Similarly, Variegated Meadowhawks have white side stripes with yellow bases, which darken with age to leave just the yellow spots.

The Importance of Color

Once you have experience identifying odonates, you can often take a bit of a shortcut to your final determination by using color. The overall color of a dragonfly or damselfly can quickly pin down the species, or at least narrow down your choices. The following table provides a helpful guide.

Color	Dragonfly	Damselfly
Green	Western Pondhawk (female or immature male)	Emerald Spreadwing River Jewelwing
Green & Blue	Common Green Darner (male)	Western Forktail (male)
Blue	Western Pondhawk (male) Blue Dasher (male)	Western Forktail (female)
Red	Meadowhawk (male) Flame Skimmer	Desert Firetail Western Red Damsel
Brown & Yellow	Four-spotted Skimmer Blue Dasher (female)	Most females except for some andromorphic individuals
Blue Spots	Darners	Bluets
Black & White Wings	Skimmers Common Whitetail	none

How to Use this Book

This book is designed to help you identify common odonates in your area. It is based on my years of experience leading field trips, and helping participants with their identifications. To this end, each species has its own two-page spread that incorporates unique features to improve your dragonflying skills (figure 34).

SPECIES ARRANGEMENT: The various species of dragonflies and damselflies are presented in order of their biological similarities to one another. Thus, darners are grouped together, as are meadowhawks, bluets, and spreadwings. This arrangement results in odonates of the same general color appearing near one another in the book.

COLOR-CODED FAMILIES: Notice that the margins of the pages have different colors. This is to make it easier to find the various odonate families. For example, red margins indicate the section of the guide devoted to meadowhawks.

SPECIES DESCRIPTION (a): Each species description starts with the official common name, the official scientific name, and an indication of whether the odonate is a percher or a flyer. You will also find information about the habitat and behavior of the species, field marks for both males and females, and comparisons with similar-looking species.

LIFE-SIZED PHOTOS (b): A unique, and very helpful, feature of this field guide is a life-size photo for each species. Thus, instead of having a numerical value for the length of a dragonfly, or a ruler showing the length, in this guide you have a photo showing the dragonfly at its actual size—as if it had landed on the page!

RANGE MAPS (c): Each spread includes a range map showing the geographic distribution of the species. The maps have been generated from the best current information, as collected by the Dragonfly Society of the Americas. Of course, infrequent visitors to our range may be seen on occasion. Examples of a few of these species are shown in figure 35, a-d.

FLIGHT SEASON CHARTS (d): These are another feature that is unique to this guide. They show the percentage of all observations of a given species that are made in a given month throughout the year. Some species have a sharply peaked distribution, while others have more extended flight seasons; some species appear early in the year, while others show up only much later. For example, the flight-season charts show that if you see a darner in May, it is almost certainly a California Darner. If you see a red dragonfly in October, it is almost sure to be an Autumn Meadowhawk.

ANNOTATED PHOTOS (e): Field marks are an important part of identification. Still, it can be hard to go from a written description of a field mark to its actual appearance on an individual dragonfly or damselfly. This guide has annotated photos with labels that show exactly where the field marks are located. The annotations also point out other features of interest, such as hamules that identify a male and ovipositors or egg scoops that identify a female.

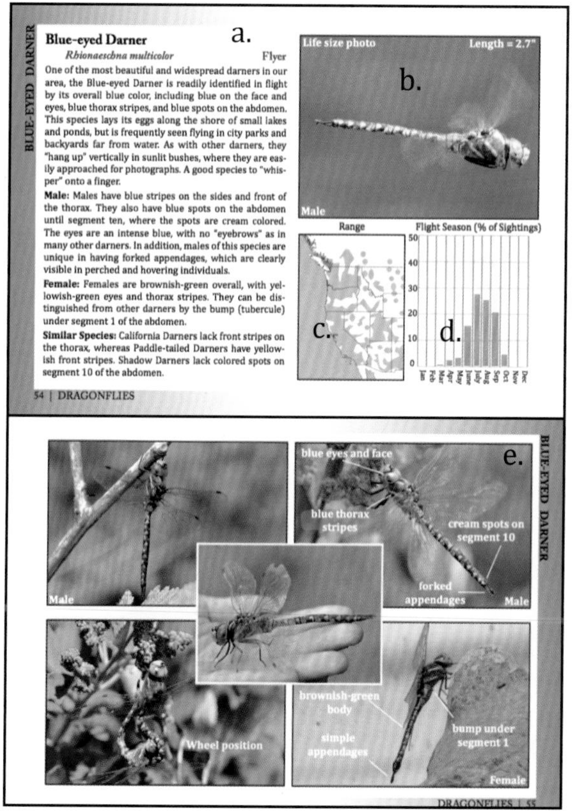
BLUE-EYED DARNER

Blue-eyed Darner a.

Rhionaeschna multicolor Flyer

One of the most beautiful and widespread darners in our area, the Blue-eyed Darner is readily identified in flight by its overall blue color, including blue on the face and eyes, blue thorax stripes, and blue spots on the abdomen. This species lays its eggs along the shore of small lakes and ponds, but is frequently seen flying in city parks and backyards far from water. As with other darners, they "hang up" vertically in sunlit bushes, where they are easily approached for photographs. A good species to "whisper" onto a finger.

Male: Males have blue stripes on the sides and front of the thorax. They also have blue spots on the abdomen until segment ten, where the spots are cream colored. The eyes are an intense blue, with no "eyebrows" as in many other darners. In addition, males of this species are unique in having forked appendages, which are clearly visible in perched and hovering individuals.

Female: Females are brownish-green overall, with yellowish-green eyes and thorax stripes. They can be distinguished from other darners by the bump (tubercule) under segment 1 of the abdomen.

Similar Species: California Darners lack front stripes on the thorax, whereas Paddle-tailed Darners have yellowish front stripes. Shadow Darners lack colored spots on segment 10 of the abdomen.

54 | DRAGONFLIES

Fig. 34.

Examples of Less Frequently Observed Species

Fig. 35a. Plateau Dragonlet.

Fig. 35b. Painted Damsel.

Fig. 35c. Blue-ringed Dancer.

Fig. 35d. White-belted Ringtail.

Dragonfly and Damselfly
Species Spreads

Black Petaltail

Tanypteryx hageni **Percher**

A large, black-and-yellow dragonfly with clear wings and well separated eyes. Found in boggy areas, mostly at high elevation, Black Petaltails are easy to approach as they perch on flat surfaces exposed to the sun, such as logs, rocks, and leaves. In addition, they frequently perch on people, a behavior that can be thought of as a "field mark" for this species. Females lay eggs in moss and mud along the shoreline, and the larvae live in burrows from which they ambush passing prey. The larvae can take up to five years to mature, due to the short growing season in their preferred habitats. Thus, a Black Petaltail may live for as much as 6 years, which is significantly longer than the typical one-year life span of other dragonflies.

Male: Males have a black body with yellow spots on the thorax and abdomen. Near the tip, the abdomen becomes all black. The eyes are dark brown and widely separated, and the face is cream colored. The wings are clear, with very long stigmas, and the appendages are petal shaped, hence the common name.

Female: Females are much like the males, but with abdomens that are thicker overall, and with a prominent ovipositor at the tip that curves upward.

Similar Species: No other species in our area has such a prominent yellow-on-black color pattern.

Life size photo   Length = 2.2"

Male

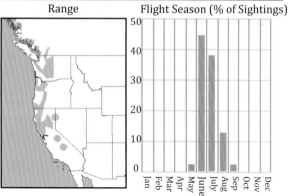

Range   Flight Season (% of Sightings)

black and yellow body

Male

"petal-shaped" appendages

Male

Male

thick abdomen

side view

ovipositor

small appendages

Female

Photo credit (both photos): Cary Kerst

Canada Darner

Aeshna canadensis **Flyer**

A good-sized darner, distinguished by the unusual shape of its thorax stripes. Males often descend into emergent vegetation along the shore of ponds and bogs in search of females, where they hover and move slowly through the vegetation. This produces audible sounds as their wings hit against the stems of vegetation; listening for this sound helps to locate them. Pairs mate in the wheel position for extended periods of time, and can be easily whispered onto a finger at this time. Individuals often perch vertically on tree trunks exposed to the sun.

Male: The key field mark for this species is the notched forward stripe on the side of the thorax. The shape of this stripe is likened to that of a slipper or a clog. A yellow spot appears behind the front stripe, and the rear stripe is wide at the top and narrows to a point at the bottom. This species has front stripes on the thorax, bluish eyes, and bluish spots along the length of the abdomen. The color spots on the 10th segment are light blue or even cream colored, and the appendages are simple.

Female: Females have thorax stripes similar to those of males, but are overall brownish-green in color.

Similar Species: California and Variable Darners lack front stripes on the thorax. Blue-eyed Darners have forked appendages and blue thorax stripes. Shadow and Paddle-tailed Darners have paddle-shaped appendages.

Male

Range

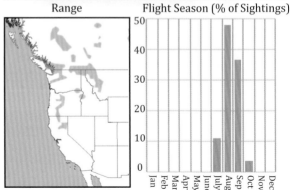

Flight Season (% of Sightings)

Male

notched side stripes

Male

Female

Photo credit (both photos): Dennis Paulson

Life size photo

Length = 2.7"

Male

simple appendages

Male

Variable Darner

Aeshna interrupta **Flyer**

The Variable Darner is distinguished by side stripes on the thorax that are of variable thickness—hence the common name of this species. Variable Darners perch more frequently than most other darners, often on the ground or on smooth vertical surfaces such as tree trunks, fence posts, and walls. Pairs fly for extended periods of time in the wheel position, and lay eggs in shoreline vegetation at ponds and small lakes. They are sometimes seen in large groups flying around a clearing as they feed.

Male: The thorax has yellow side stripes that are thinner in the middle than at the ends. The stripes are sometimes broken—or interrupted—as indicated in the scientific name. Front stripes on the thorax are minimal, or absent altogether. The 10th segment of the abdomen is cream-colored, the appendages are simple, and the blue stripe on the top of segment 2 is partial. Young individuals have brown eyes, which turn blue with age.

Female: Females have the same basic stripe pattern as males, but on a brownish-yellow body.

Similar Species: Paddle-tailed Darners have blue spots on the 10th segment of the abdomen. Shadow Darners have a 10th segment that is black. The California Darner has side stripes on the thorax that do not pinch in. The Blue-eyed Darner has forked appendages and blue side stripes on the thorax.

Male

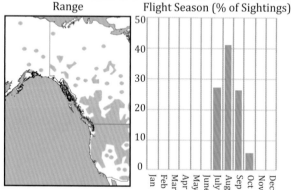

Range

Flight Season (% of Sightings)

Male

Life size photo   Length = 2.6"

Male

variable width side stripes

cream spots on segment 10

simple appendages

Male

brown and yellow body

Female

Photo credit: Pierre Deviche

Paddle-tailed Darner

Aeshna palmata   **Flyer**

The Paddle-tailed Darner, also known as the "Happy-face" Dragonfly, is a truly remarkable insect. Not only does it have an incredible "happy-face" appearance, but it is also the most proficient species at splash-dunking—plunging into the water as many as 8 times in a row to bathe. Following a series of splash-dunks, it gains about 10 feet of altitude and does a spin-dry, in which it tumbles head-over-heels at 1,000 rpm to shed water in a burst of spray. During mating, the pair remains in the wheel position for an extended period of time. After mating, the female lays eggs in logs or vegetation on the shore of lakes or ponds, often with the male attached in tandem.

Male: Males have a row of blue spots on the abdomen. The spots get larger near the tip, and completely cover segment 10. The appendages are paddle-shaped, as the name of this species suggests. On the front of the thorax are yellowish stripes that are pinched in at the top. In addition, the blue stripe on the top of segment 2 of the abdomen is thin and straight.

Female: Females are similar, but are yellowish brown in overall color and with simple appendages.

Similar Species: Shadow Darners lack blue spots on segment 10 of the abdomen. Variable and California Darners have cream spots on segment 10 and simple appendages. Blue-eyed Darners have forked appendages.

"Happy-face" Dragonfly

Male

Range   Flight Season (% of Sightings)

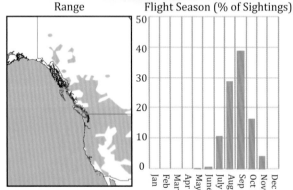

Life size photo   Length = 2.8"

thin
straight line
on segment 2

paddle-shaped
appendages

blue on
segment 10

Male

Male - female
in wheel position

happy face
with eyebrows
and smile

front
stripes yellowish,
pinched in at top

Male

Male

Shadow Darner

Aeshna umbrosa   **Flyer**

A large darner found at lakes, ponds, and streams. It is notable for favoring shady spots along the shore. In fact, this species often patrols shaded areas, and extends its territory as the shadows lengthen. Though spending much of their time on the wing, Shadow Darners rest by hanging vertically in shoreline bushes exposed to the sun. They can be easily whispered onto a finger, where they will remain happily for long periods of time.

Male: Shadow Darners have clear wings, paddle-shaped appendages, small blue spots on the abdomen, and no blue spots at all on segment 10. This gives the body an overall dark appearance. The side stripes on the thorax are yellowish, with a thick black border. The front stripes are greenish, and wide at the top. In addition, the blue stripe on the top of segment 2 of the abdomen is wide in the middle, giving it a spindle shape.

Female: Females have similar stripes and spots, but are brownish in color. One or more of the appendages are often broken off.

Similar Species: Paddle-tailed Darners have yellowish front stripes on the thorax that pinch in at the top, a thin blue line on the top of segment 2, and blue spots that get larger toward the tip of the abdomen, covering segment 10. Variable and California Darners have simple appendages, Blue-eyed Darners have forked appendages.

Male

Range

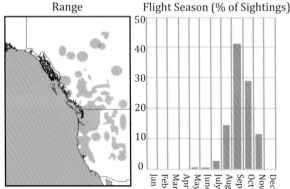
Flight Season (% of Sightings)

greenish front stripes, wide at top

Male

spindle stripe on segment 2

small blue spots

black segment 10

Male

Life size photo

Length=2.8"

paddle-shaped appendages

Male

wide segment 3

simple appendages

Female

Walker's Darner

Aeshna walkeri   **Flyer**

Walker's Darner is unusual in that it prefers small streams to the lakes and ponds preferred by other darners in our range. Females lay eggs along the banks of streams on moss or roots of shoreline vegetation. Males patrol up and down streams looking for females, or visit clearings near the stream to feed. Walker's Darners appear to fly incessantly, but they perch about as often as other darners. They are less conspicuous when perched, however, because they often land in trees well above head height.

Male: Males are unique among the darners in our range because of the whitish color of both the face and the stripes on the thorax. They have blue spots on top of the abdomen, except for segment 10 which is mostly black with a thin blue stripe at the terminal end. The blue stripe on top of segment 2 of the abdomen is wider at the rear, and narrows toward the front.

Female: Females are similar in stripe pattern to males, but are brownish to greenish in overall color, which gives them a cryptic appearance.

Similar Species: Paddle-tailed Darners have yellowish stripes on the thorax and large blue spots on segment 10 of the abdomen. Shadow Darners have greenish front stripes on the thorax. Variable Darners have simple appendages. Blue-eyed Darners have forked appendages.

Male

Range

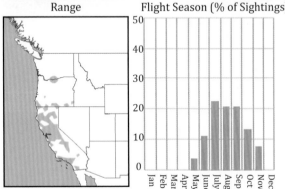

Flight Season (% of Sightings

Male

Photo credit: Cary Kerst

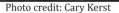

Life size photo
Length = 2.6"

Male

white side stripes

paddle-shaped appendages

Male

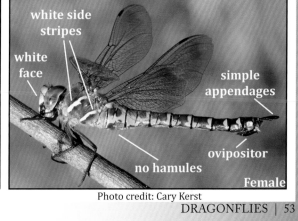

white side stripes

white face

simple appendages

ovipositor

no hamules

Female

Photo credit: Cary Kerst

DRAGONFLIES | 53

California Darner

Rhionaeschna californica   **Flyer**

The earliest flying and smallest darner in our range—so small, in fact, that it can be mistaken for a skimmer. This species is more likely to land on the ground, or on a stem close to the ground, than other darners—thus, an early season darner resting on the ground is probably a California Darner. These darners are also noted for preying on damselflies, especially pairs flying in tandem. Females lay eggs with an ovipositor on logs or stems along the shore of a small lake or pond.

Male: The male California Darner has blue eyes, and a gray face with a dark horizontal line across the middle. Appendages are simple, and the tenth segment of the abdomen has cream-colored spots. The key field mark is the absence, or near absence, of front stripes on the thorax. In addition, the forward side stripe on the thorax has a black border on the rear edge, and tapers near the top.

Female: Females have similar stripes to the males, including a lack of stripes on the front of the thorax. They are generally greenish-brown in color.

Similar Species: The only other darner in our range that lacks front stripes on the thorax is the Variable Darner. However, the Variable Darner has side stripes on the thorax that vary in thickness, and sometimes pinch off in the middle.

Life size photo   Length = 2.4"

Male

Range   Flight Season (% of Sightings)

Male

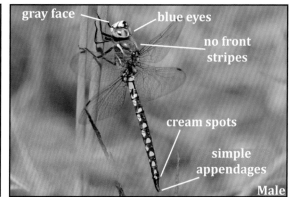

gray face

blue eyes

no front stripes

cream spots

simple appendages

Male

Male

no front stripes

Female

Blue-eyed Darner

Rhionaeschna multicolor **Flyer**

One of the most beautiful and widespread darners in our area, the Blue-eyed Darner is readily identified in flight by its overall blue color, including blue on the face and eyes, blue thorax stripes, and blue spots on the abdomen. This species lays its eggs along the shore of small lakes and ponds, but is frequently seen flying in city parks and backyards far from water. As with other darners, they "hang up" vertically in sunlit bushes, where they are easily approached for photographs. A good species to "whisper" onto a finger.

Male: Males have blue stripes on the sides and front of the thorax. They also have blue spots on the abdomen until segment 10, where the spots are cream colored. The eyes are an intense blue, with no "eyebrows" as in many other darners. In addition, males of this species are unique in having forked appendages, which are clearly visible in perched and hovering individuals.

Female: Females are brownish-green overall, with yellowish-green eyes and thorax stripes. They can be distinguished from other darners by the bump (tubercle) under segment 1 of the abdomen.

Similar Species: California Darners lack front stripes on the thorax, whereas Paddle-tailed Darners have yellowish front stripes. Shadow Darners lack colored spots on segment 10 of the abdomen.

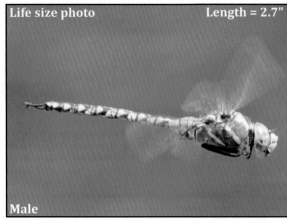

Life size photo · Length = 2.7" · Male

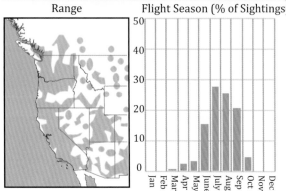

Range · Flight Season (% of Sightings)

Male

blue eyes and face

blue thorax stripes

cream spots on segment 10

forked appendages

Male

Wheel position

brownish-green body

simple appendages

bump under segment 1

Female

DRAGONFLIES | 57

Common Green Darner

Anax junius   **Flyer**

The Common Green Darner is the largest dragonfly in our range. Its vigorous flight and distinctive color pattern—green on the front of the body, blue on the rear—make it easy to identify in flight. Large and aggressive, the Common Green Darner has been observed eating prey as large as Eight-spotted Skimmers. Pairs remain in the wheel position for extended periods, providing a good opportunity to whisper them onto your finger. They stay attached in tandem as the female lays eggs in floating or shoreline vegetation, sometimes submerging up to her thorax. This species, which is one of the few known to migrate, is seen almost everywhere, from lakes and ponds to marshes and streams.

Male: The front third of the body, including the head and thorax, is green. The abdomen is mostly blue, with a dark stripe running down the center of the top surface, getting wider near the tip. The appendages are simple, and a "target"-like pattern can be seen on the top of the face, between the eyes.

Female: Similar in most respects to the male, though with an abdomen that is brownish-tan rather than blue.

Similar Species: Other darners are similar in overall body shape, but none have the Common Green Darner's large size and unique blue-green color pattern.

Life size photo   Length = 3.0"

Male

Range   Flight Season (% of Sightings)

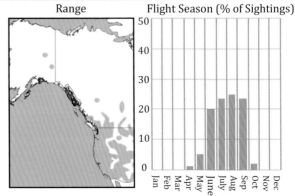

Male - female in wheel position

green head and thorax

mostly blue abdomen

black stripe

Male

Teneral (freshly emerged) female

brownish abdomen

green head and thorax

Female laying eggs

Pacific Clubtail

Gomphus kurilis   Percher

A large, boldly-patterned dragonfly with a distinctive "club-like" widening at the tip of the abdomen—hence the name clubtail. This species perches on bushes, or on the ground, near the shore of ponds, lakes, streams, and rivers. Frequently seen in the foothills at elevations up to about 5000 ft. Pairs generally perch in trees as they mate, often at or above head height. Females lay eggs alone by tapping the tip of their abdomen in the water as they fly along a shoreline. As is typical of clubtails, the eyes in this species do not meet in the middle.

Male: The abdomen in this species is black, with a series of bright yellow "spear points" on top pointing toward the tip. A row of yellow spots decorate the sides of the abdomen. Bold yellow stripes are prominent on the front and sides of the thorax. The eyes are bluish gray, and are relatively small for a dragonfly—they don't touch in the middle, but are separated by a yellow bar. The face is the same bright yellow seen on the rest of the body.

Female: Females are similar to males, but with larger yellow spots on the abdomen. They also lack the extreme widening at the tip of the abdomen.

Similar Species: Grappletails lack the yellow spear points on top the abdomen, and have distinctive grapple-shaped appendages

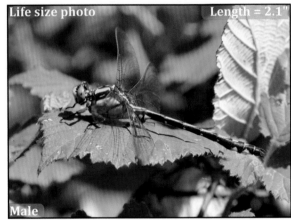

Life size photo   Length = 2.1"

Male

Range

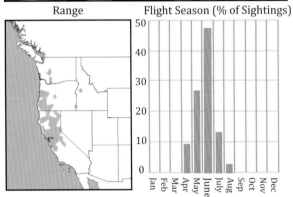

Flight Season (% of Sightings)

Male

- eyes separated by yellow bar
- bright yellow face

Male

- yellow spear-points pointing backwards
- yellow stripes on thorax
- club-shaped tip

Female

- extensive yellow on abdomen
- small appendages

Female

- broad base to abdomen
- no club at tip

Columbia Clubtail

Gomphus lynnae   Percher

Discovered in 1971 on the Yakima River in arid south-central Washington, and named by Dennis Paulson in 1983, this is the most recently described dragonfly species in our range. More sightings have been reported in Washington since then, together with several observations in eastern Oregon; a single sighting is on the record in both Nevada and New Mexico. This bold, dramatic-looking dragonfly is easy to approach and photograph, and can be quite abundant in the isolated locations where it occurs. Individuals of both sexes generally perch on the ground, or low in a bush.

Male: Males are distinguished by a large expanded "club" at the tip of the abdomen; they also have prominent, outspread appendages. Segments 3-6 of the abdomen have rear-pointing, tan spear tips on top; segments 7-9 have bright yellow spots on the tops and sides. The eyes are light blue, the face is yellow, and the thorax has yellow stripes on the front and sides. A light powder-blue pruinosity develops on the thorax and base of the abdomen with age.

Female: Similar to the males, but with a less pronounced "club" at the tip of the abdomen, and tiny appendages.

Similar Species: The Pacific Clubtail lacks pruinosity, and its thorax is mostly yellow on the sides.

Life size photo   Length = 2.2"

Male

Range

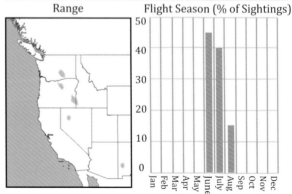

Flight Season (% of Sightings)

blue eyes, yellow face

light pruinosity

Male

club-shaped tip, prominent appendages

tan spear-points, pointing backwards

Male

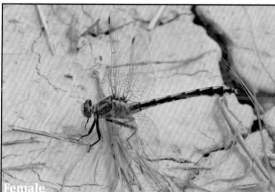

Female

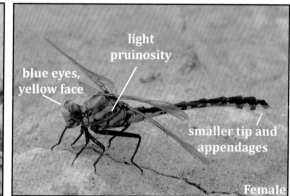

light pruinosity

blue eyes, yellow face

smaller tip and appendages

Female

Pale Snaketail

Ophiogomphus severus   **Percher**

An impressive green, black, and yellow dragonfly with a noticeably expanded "club-like" tip on the abdomen. Even so, this species can be quite inconspicuous when perched on the rocky shore of a stream or river—in fact, they can seem to "vanish" when sitting on a gravely surface. They like to perch near riffles facing the water, often with their abdomens elevated as they look for prey or potential mates. Mating in the wheel position takes place for an extended period of time. Females lay eggs by tapping the tip of the abdomen on the surface of the water, unattended by the male.

Male: Males of this species have an impressive array of colors. Their eyes are sky blue, their face is light green, and their thorax is pale green. The most distinctive field mark is a brown oblong spot on the shoulder of the thorax. The wings are clear, except for a yellow vein along the leading edge. The abdomen is black, with extensive bold yellow spots along its length, and yellow along the edges of the "club-shaped" tip.

Female: Females are similar to males, but with a whitish stripe low on the side of the abdomen. They often perch away from the water on low bushes.

Similar Species: Great Basin Snaketails have a wide brown stripe on the front of the thorax and broad brown stripes on the shoulders.

Life size photo   Length = 2.0"

Male

Range   Flight Season (% of Sightings)

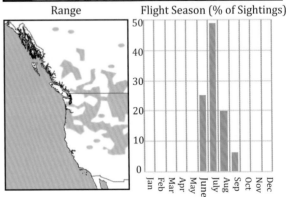

Male

pale
green
thorax

brown oblong spot

Male

Male

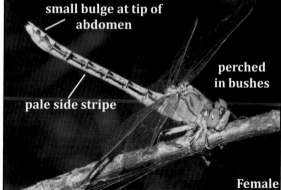

small bulge at tip of
abdomen

pale side stripe

perched
in bushes

Female

Photo credit: Netta Smith

Great Basin Snaketail

Ophiogomphus morrisoni **Percher**

A striking dragonfly with bold colors and patterns, Great Basin Snaketails often perch on the ground or in low bushes where they are frequently harassed by Northern and Boreal Bluets. Adding to their impressive appearance are the expanded "club" at the tip of the tail and the sky-blue color of the eyes. This species tends to mate while perched high in a tree. After mating, the female lays eggs by flying low over the surface of a lake or a swift-flowing stream, tapping the water with her abdomen as she goes.

Male: Males are almost equally brown and yellow in color, with the yellow markings standing out in dramatic fashion against the brown background. The eyes are a beautiful blue, the face is bright yellow, and the abdomen—which is expanded into a "club" at the tip—has both brown and yellow on every segment. The key distinguishing feature for this species is the shape of the thorax stripes. The front of the thorax has a broad yellow stripe that curls around near the wings and heads back downward, enclosing a brown stripe.

Female: Females are similar to males, except the tip of the abdomen is not as expanded. In addition, their abdomens are thicker overall, with a white stripe along the lower side.

Similar Species: The Pale Snaketail has a pale green thorax with an oblong brown spot on the shoulders.

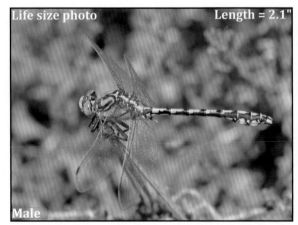

Life size photo — Length = 2.1"

Male

Range

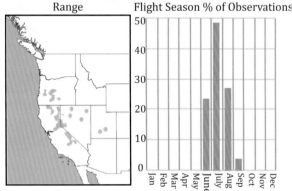

Flight Season % of Observations

Male—harrassed by bluet

curving yellow stripe enclosing brown stripe

club-like tail

Male

Male

thick abdomen

white stripe low on side of abdomen

Female

Grappletail

Octogomphus specularis　　　　　　　　**Percher**

A unique dragonfly with pincher-like appendages. Individuals of this species live on streams and creeks, where they can be locally numerous. They frequently perch on logs or rocks in a stream, but also on vegetation along the shore. Females often perch away from the shore when not laying eggs, and are sometimes found in dark forested areas. Eggs are laid by tapping the water rapidly along the shore of a stream. Grappletails are relatively tame, and can be approached for photographs. Both sexes are yellowish when young, but darken with age.

Male: Males have large and impressive appendages that are wider than the abdomen and point inward like the prongs of a grappling hook. The appendages are made even more prominent by their bright yellow color. A bold yellow stripe runs down the center of the thorax, from behind the head to the abdomen, and the sides of the thorax are bright yellow. The abdomen has small yellow markings on a black background, including a distinctive round yellow spot on the 10th segment. Grappletails have yellow faces, and eyes that are bluish or brown above and yellow below.

Female: Females look much like males, but lack the impressive appendages.

Similar Species: No other species in our range has this color pattern, and none have similar appendages.

Life size photo　　　　　　　　Length = 2.0"

Male

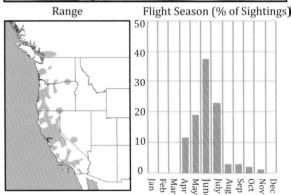

Range　　　　　　Flight Season (% of Sightings)

Male

bold yellow
thorax stripes

grappling hook
appendages

Male

Female

Photo credit: Ray Bruun

bold yellow
thorax stripes

small
appendages

Female

Photo credit: Ray Bruun

American Emerald

Cordulia shurtleffii   **Percher**

A mostly black dragonfly with emerald green eyes that is found on small lakes and ponds. When observed flying low over the water at a distance, the eyes flash a brilliant green every time the dragonfly turns toward the observer. After mating, the male guards the female by flying in tandem with her. As she flies, the female produces a growing yellow mass of eggs at the tip of her abdomen, which becomes clearly visible as it gets larger and larger. When the egg mass reaches a significant size, the female dips the tip of her abdomen into the water to deposit the eggs. Fish are on the lookout to grab the egg mass, and they are often successful.

Male: The eyes have an incredible emerald green color, which immediately identifies it as an emerald species. The thorax is brownish, with a metallic iridescent-green cast. The key feature for this species is the single white ring at the base of the abdomen, on segment 3. The abdomen is spindle shaped—that is, expanded outward in the middle, and narrow at either end.

Female: Females are similar to males, but with less intense colors. The female's abdomen is cylindrical in shape, and lacks a narrow "waist" on segment 3.

Similar Species: The Ringed Emerald has white rings at the base of each abdominal segment. The Mountain Emerald has no white rings on the abdomen.

Life size photo   Length = 1.9"

Male

Range   Flight Season (% of Sightings)

white ring at base of abdomen

spindle-shaped abdomen

Male

intensely green eyes

Male

metallic green iridescence

white ring

wide base of abdomen

Female

Ringed Emerald

Somatochlora albicincta   **Percher**

Ringed Emeralds have brilliant green eyes, as one would expect in a member of the emerald family. The eyes are so bright they give off a flash of green every time an individual flies toward an observer. Ringed Emeralds are also named for the prominent white rings on each segment of the abdomen. These features make Ringed Emeralds easy to identify, even on the wing at a considerable distance. Males fly back and forth along the shores of ponds and small lakes. Females tap the water to lay their eggs, which come out in a thin ribbon of several eggs, like miniature frog eggs. The ribbon twists and turns as it slowly drifts to the bottom. Egg-laying females are sometimes guarded by a male, but are often unaccompanied.

Male: Males have green eyes, a black face that is yellow on the sides, a metallic dark green thorax, and clear wings. The most distinctive feature is the series of bold white rings at the base of the abdominal segments, which gives this species its name. The background color of the abdomen is black.

Female: Females of this species look much like the males, though their colors are slightly more muted.

Similar Species: American Emeralds have only a single white ring at the base of the abdomen. Mountain Emeralds have no white rings.

Life size photo   Length = 1.9"

Male

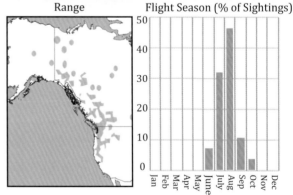

Range   Flight Season (% of Sightings)

emerald green eyes

metallic green thorax

Male

white rings on abdomen

Male

Female

Photo credit: Dennis Paulson

Female laying eggs

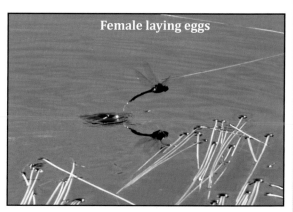

Female laying eggs

Mountain Emerald

Somatochlora semicircularis   **Percher**

Mountain Emeralds are relatively small, dark dragonflies with beautiful emerald green eyes. They are found on small lakes and ponds with densely-vegetated shores, often at high elevation. Mountain Emeralds perch in vegetation along the shore, either near the ground or high in neighboring trees. They often remain perched for extended periods of time, making for easy observation. Mating pairs are observed to fly in tandem for as long as half an hour. Egg laying is done by the female tapping the water a few times in one location, then tapping a few times in a nearby location, and so on. Males guard their mates by hovering above the female, and chasing away any rivals.

Male: Males are mostly dark, with intense emerald green eyes. Their abdomens are almost entirely black, with no white rings at any location. The thorax has an iridescent green sheen, as is typical of all emeralds. In addition, the sides of the thorax have two oblong, pale yellow spots. These spots are the key distinguishing feature for identifying this species.

Female: Females are similar in appearance to males, though with less intense colors.

Similar Species: American Emeralds have a white ring at the base of the abdomen. Ringed Emeralds have a prominent series of white rings at the base of each abdominal segment.

Life size photo   Length = 2.0"

Male

Range

Flight Season (% of Sightings)

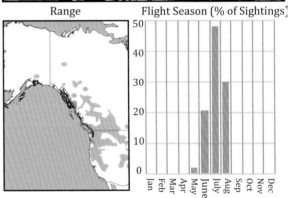

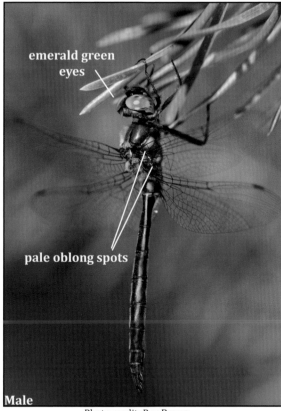

emerald green eyes

pale oblong spots

Male

Photo credit: Ray Bruun

solid black abdomen

Male

Male

Female

Photo credit: Dennis Paulson

Spiny Baskettail

Epitheca spinigera   **Flyer**

A small, dark brown dragonfly that is similar to the Beaverpond Baskettail, but differs in the shape of the appendages—which taper smoothly to a point in this species. Males like to patrol a clearing near a small lake or pond, often following a well-defined route at chest height, never seeming to land. When a female is ready to lay eggs, she perches on a bush or small tree near the shore and slowly extrudes eggs to form a yellow mass at the tip of her abdomen. She then flies low over the water, looking for a good place to drop off her eggs. Fish often gulp down the egg mass as soon as it is deposited.

Male: Males are slender, dark brown, with clear wings. Their eyes are emerald green, lavender, or red on top, depending on age, and the face is dull yellow. The abdomen is brown with yellow stripes along the sides. The key distinguishing feature is the shape of the appendages, which in this species are simple in shape.

Female: Females are similar to males in this species, though generally somewhat lighter brown in overall color. They can be distinguished from the males by the lack of hamules under segment 2 of the abdomen.

Similar Species: In Beaverpond Baskettails, the male appendages bend downward at right angles at the tip, in the shape of a pistol pointing forward.

Life size photo   Length = 1.8"

Female

Range

Flight Season (% of Sightings)

simple appendages

Male

Photo credit: Cary Kerst

spindle-shaped abdomen

Male

Photo credit: Cary Kerst

Female

Photo credit: Cary Kerst

egg mass

Female

Beaverpond Baskettail

Epitheca canis   Percher

Beaverpond Baskettails perch frequently and are relatively easy to approach for photographs. They are found on rivers and slow-moving streams, in addition to ponds and lakes. Males have distinctive appendages, and both sexes have small dark patches at the base of the wings. When a female lays eggs she develops a yellowish egg mass at the tip of the abdomen, which she then taps into the water to deposit the entire mass at once. Fish are often on the lookout for this tasty treat, so the females may zig and zag about the pond for a considerable amount of time before finally depositing the eggs. Even so, fish are often on hand to immediately gulp them down.

Male: Males are mostly black, brown and yellow in color. The abdomen is black down the center, but with yellowish stripes along the sides. The abdomen is also spindle shaped—wider in the middle than at either end. Eye color varies from green to a lovely lavender. Male appendages project downward at the tip, giving a shape reminiscent of a pistol pointing forward. This distinctive feature is readily visible with binoculars.

Female: Similar to males, but with simple appendages.

Similar Species: The appendages of Spiny Baskettails are simple in shape in both the male and the female. Otherwise, the two species are similar in appearance.

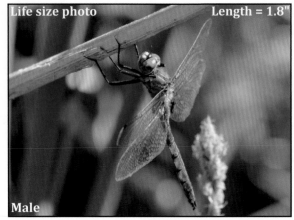

Life size photo   Length = 1.8"

Male

Range

Flight Season (% of Sightings)

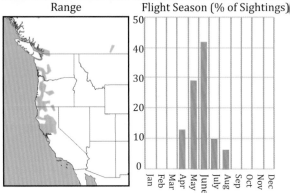

Male

brown, black, and yellow body

hamules

"pistol-shaped" appendages

Male

Photo credit: Cary Kerst

Male

spindle-shaped abdomen

Photo credit: Cary Kerst

simple appendages

no hamules

Female

Photo credit: Cary Kerst

Common Whitetail

Plathemis lydia   **Percher**

A flashy dragonfly that occupies a range of habitats, from marshy bogs and small lakes to muddy cow ponds and ditches. Common Whitetails generally perch on a shoreline rock or fallen log, or on low-lying vegetation when bare ground is not available. Males use their white abdomens to threaten rivals. When males chase one another, the pursuing male elevates its abdomen to make it visible to its rival, while the pursued male depresses its abdomen to show it to its pursuer. Mating is brief, due to the difficulty of attaining the wheel position with such stout abdomens. After mating, the male hovers over the female and chases all intruders. Females dip the abdomen into the water to lay eggs, often flipping a drop of egg-laden water onto the surface of floating algae.

Male: The abdomen is wide, stout, and covered with an intensely bluish-white pruinosity. In young males the abdomen is brown with whitish side stripes. All four wings have a large central black patch, with smaller patches of black and white near the base.

Female: The abdomen is brown with whitish side stripes that curve inward on their forward ends. Each wing has three small dark spots, including a dark spot at the tip.

Similar Species: Eight-spotted and Twelve-spotted Skimmer males have smaller dark wing patches. Females have straight yellow stripes on the abdomen.

Life size photo   Length = 1.8"

Male

Range   Flight Season (% of Sightings)

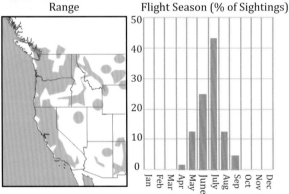

Male

large black
wing patches

white abdomen

Male

Immature male

small
dark
spots

dark
wing tips

whitish side stripes

Female

Chalk-fronted Corporal

Ladona julia — **Percher**

A stocky, distinctive dragonfly with unique thorax markings. Chalk-fronted Corporals tend to perch on logs in the sun, as well as on bare patches of ground. Closer to the shore they perch on vegetation as they scan the waters of a small lake or pond, often in the mountains or foothills. They perch for extended periods of time, and are a bit wary of people. Mating in the wheel position is brief, due to their stout abdomens. After mating the male guards the egg-laying female by hovering above her at a height of a few feet.

Male: Males are easy to identify due to the white pruinosity on the front of the thorax and at the base of the abdomen. The pruinosity on the thorax forms two broad parallel bars, like the insignia for a corporal. The sides of the thorax are black, the eyes are dark brown, and the face is black. All four wings are clear, except for small dark brown patches near the base.

Female: Brownish overall, with somewhat lighter color on the front of the thorax and at the base of the abdomen. Older females become increasingly pruinose, almost like the males. Females have smaller appendages than males.

Similar Species: No other species has this color pattern. A young female corporal might look like a Four-spotted Skimmer, but the skimmer has larger dark patches with white veins on the hindwings.

Life size photo — Length = 1.7" — Male

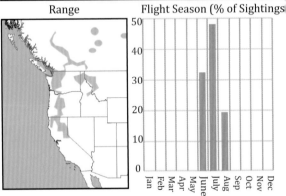
Range — Flight Season (% of Sightings)

Male

"corporal" marks

dark eyes and face

pruinosity at base of abdomen

Male

Immature male

small appendages

brownish overall

Female

Four-spotted Skimmer

Libellula quadrimaculata **Percher**

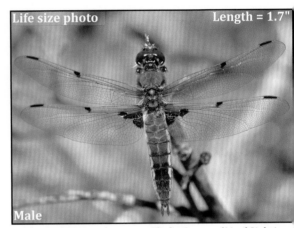

Life size photo — Length = 1.7"

Male

The Four-spotted Skimmer is a small but active dragonfly, and the only golden-brown dragonfly in our range. Sometimes seen in great numbers at ponds and lakes, the males and females are practically identical in this species. Males aggressively guard their territory, chasing all other nearby dragonflies, even large darners. Mating in the wheel position is brief, due to the rather stocky, inflexible abdomens in this species. After mating the female descends to the water, where she taps vigorously as she lays eggs. The male hovers nearby, fending off intruders.

Male: This species is named for the dark spots at the center (nodus) of the leading edge of the wings. The stigmas aren't counted as spots because all dragonflies have them. When young, this dragonfly is a rich golden brown, with large yellow stripes bordered in black on the sides of the thorax, and yellow stripes along the sides of the abdomen. These colors darken with age. The tip of the abdomen is black, and the base of the hindwings have large brown wing patches with white veins.

Female: Females are practically identical to males. The main difference is that the base of the abdomen (segment 2) is smooth on the underside in the female.

Similar Species: No other species in our range is brown with dark spots at the nodus of the wings.

Range

Flight Season (% of Sightings)

Male

hamules

dark wing patch

dark spots at nodus

yellow side stripes

Male

egg scoop

no hamules

Female

dark spots at nodus

brown abdomen with black tip

Female

Flame Skimmer

Libellula saturata **Percher**

A brilliantly-colored dragonfly that flies strongly and perches in conspicuous locations. With their intense red color on their bodies and wings, Flame Skimmers are always noticed at any pond, lake, or stream where they occur. Pairs mate briefly, due to their stocky abdomens, and females lay eggs as the male hovers to guard. When females tap the water to lay eggs, they flick the tip of their abdomen forward, sending an egg-laden drop of water out in front of them.

Male: The body is red from head to tail, the eyes are red, and the wings have a reddish-orange wash that extends out past the nodus to cover more than half of the wing. At the base of each wing is a roughly rectangular area where the reddish color is much darker. A central light line runs along the front of the thorax, though it becomes darker and less distinct with age.

Female: The female Flame Skimmer is similar to the male, but with a brownish-red color. The light line along the center of the thorax is more pronounced in the female, extending between the wings to the rear of the thorax and onto the base of the abdomen. The abdomen flanges outward noticeably at the egg scoop, near the tip.

Similar Species: Cardinal Meadowhawks are smaller, with smaller colored patches in the wings and white spots on the sides of the thorax.

Life size photo — Length = 2.2" — Male

Range

Flight Season (% of Sighting)

Male

dark red wing bars

red eyes

extensive red in wings

red body

Male

large egg scoop

Female

brownish red eyes

brownish orange body

large egg scoop

Female

Eight-spotted Skimmer

Libellula forensis   **Percher**

The Eight-spotted Skimmer is a showy dragonfly of lakes, ponds and streams. It is easily identified by its flashy black and white wings. Male Eight-spotted Skimmers patrol a stretch of shoreline, and return to one or two favorite perches. They glide extensively in flight, rocking back and forth like a hawk. Mating is brief, due to their rather stubby abdomens. Females lay eggs by tapping the water, with the male hovering nearby.

Male: The wings have eight black spots—for which the species is named—and eight white spots. The abdomen is brown with yellow stripes along the edges in young males, but it quickly turns pruinose blue with age. When the female grasps the male's abdomen during mating, some of the pruinosity is scraped off, leaving a dark patch. The eyes and face are dark brown, and the thorax has yellow side stripes.

Female: Females also have eight black spots on the wing, but the wings are transparent between the black spots. The abdomen is dark brown, with straight yellow stripes along the outside edges. The eyes and face are dark brown, and the thorax has yellow side stripes.

Similar Species: Twelve-spotted Skimmers have an additional dark spot at the tip of each wing. Female Common Whitetails have yellowish-white side stripes on their abdomens that curve inward at the forward end.

Life size photo   Length = 2.0"

Male

Range

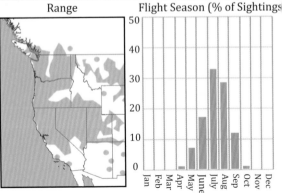

Flight Season (% of Sightings)

beginning pruinosity on abdomen

Immature male

eight white spots on wings

eight black spots on wings

pruinose blue abdomen

Male

Female

eight black spots on wings

straight yellow stripes

Female

DRAGONFLIES | 89

Twelve-spotted Skimmer

Libellula pulchella   **Percher**

The Twelve-spotted Skimmer is a close relative of the Eight-spotted Skimmer, but has an extra black spot at the tip of each wing. The species is named for the black spots because both sexes have them. These dragonflies are just as prominent as their cousins, perching on favored stems near the shore of ponds and small lakes. They glide frequently in flight and strike photogenic poses when perched. Mating is brief, due to the rather stubby abdomens of this species. The female lays eggs by tapping the water with the tip of her abdomen, guarded by a hovering male.

Male: The wings of males have one black spot at the base, one at the nodus (center), and one at the tip. Males also have white patches at the base of the wings, and between the black spots. The abdomen is brown with yellow side stripes in young individuals, turning pruinose blue with age. The eyes are dark brown, the face is brown, and the thorax is brown with two yellow side stripes.

Female: Females lack the white patches in the wings, but have the twelve black spots. Their abdomens are brown, with straight yellow side stripes.

Similar Species: Eight-spotted Skimmers lack the black spots at the tips of the wings. Female Common Whitetails have whitish side stripes on the abdomen that curve inward at their forward ends.

Life size photo   Length = 2.1"

Male

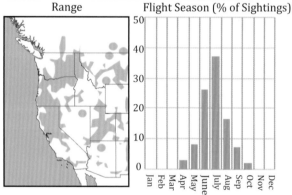

Range   Flight Season (% of Sightings)

yellow side stripes

Immature male

12 black spots

pruinose abdomen

yellow side stripes

Male

Male

brown abdomen with yellow side stripes

Female

Photo credit: Pierre Deviche

DRAGONFLIES | 91

Widow Skimmer

Libellula luctuosa   **Percher**

Widow Skimmers are conspicuous and striking, with a prominent black and white pattern on the wings. They are light on the wing, flying back and forth in their territory with much gliding, and they return over and over to a favorite stem or bush. Males make a showy spectacle on their perch, and keep a close watch for rivals and potential mates. Mating in the wheel position is brief, due to the rather inflexible abdomen in this species. Females lay eggs either alone, or with a male guarding nearby. The common name for this species comes from the dark "cloak-like" black patches in the wings.

Male: Males of this species are easily identified by the black and white pattern in the wings. Black patches extend from the base of the wings to the halfway point (the nodus), beyond which the wings are pruinose white. The eyes and face are dark brown; the thorax and abdomen are pruinose light blue.

Female: Females also have the dark wing patches, but theirs are more brownish and transparent. The wings have a light brown wash at the tips, but lack pruinosity. The abdomen is black down the middle, bordered with yellow stripes on either side.

Similar Species: Eight-spotted and Twelve-spotted Skimmers have small dark wing spots. Common Whitetails have black patches in the middle of the wings.

Life size photo   Length = 1.8"

Male

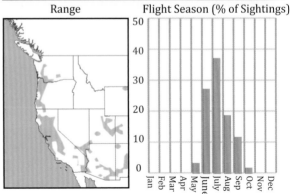

Range   Flight Season (% of Sightings)

Male

large dark wing patches and pruinosity

light-blue abdomen

Male

Immature male

black abdomen with yellow side stripes

Female

Photo credit: Pierre Deviche

Dot-tailed Whiteface

Leucorrhinia intacta **Percher**

A small black dragonfly whose chalk-white face and yellow dot on the tail (abdomen) are distinctive. This dragonfly is closely associated with lily pads, more so than any other in our range. Male Dot-tailed Whitefaces like to perch on pads to survey their territory, and pairs often rest on pads as they mate in the wheel position. They also perch on shoreline vegetation, especially females who spend much of their time away from the water's edge. Females lay eggs by tapping the water, with males hovering nearby to guard. Eggs are generally laid in shallow water where a gravely bottom can be seen.

Male: Males have a brilliant white face, jet black eyes, and a black body with a square yellow dot on segment 7 of the abdomen. The white face reflects in the black eyes, giving the eyes a whitish cast. White body hairs contrast with the black body, particularly on the front of the thorax and the underside of the abdomen. Young males have a row of yellow spots along the abdomen which darken with age to show just a single spot. The wings are clear except for light colored veins that extend beyond the stigmas.

Female: Females have a dark body, with a prominent row of yellow spots along the top of the abdomen. The eyes are dark brown, the face is white, and the wings are clear.

Similar Species: Black Meadowhawks have multiple yellow spots on the abdomen and a black face.

Life size photo Length = 1.2"

Male

Range

Flight Season (% of Sightings)

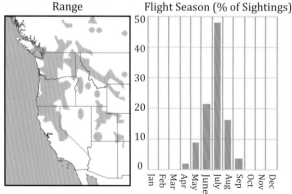

Male

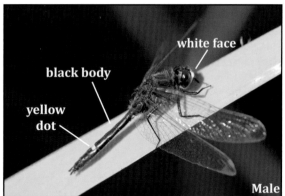

white face

black body

yellow dot

Male

Male - female in wheel position

dark brown body

yellow dot

white face

Female

Hudsonian Whiteface

Leucorrhinia hudsonica   Percher

The Hudsonian Whiteface is a rather small, delicate black-and-red dragonfly, typically found along the shore of marshy lakes and bogs, often near lily pads. Look for them to bask in the sun on prominent logs or rocks. Mating lasts for an extended period of time. Egg laying typically occurs with the female tapping the water as the male hovers nearby, but sometimes with the male remaining attached in tandem.

Male: Males have extensive brilliant red markings on the top, front, and sides of the thorax, and on top of the abdomen out to segment 7. The red markings start off yellow in young individuals, and become increasingly red with age. Males also have the typical chalk-white face of whitefaces, and dark brown eyes. Additional features of both sexes of this species are light yellow wing veins that extend beyond the stigmas—giving the wings a whitish-yellow tip. The hindwings have a small black patch near the base, with contrasting red veins.

Female: Females are similar to males, with the same basic pattern of colored spots on the body, but with markings that are yellow rather than red. Females also have white faces, dark wing patches near the base of the hindwings, and light wing veins at the tip of the wings.

Similar Species: The Dot-tailed Whiteface lacks the red markings on the thorax and abdomen.

Life size photo   Length = 1.2"

Male

Range

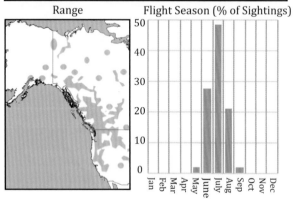

Flight Season (% of Sightings)

white face

Male

white face

red on thorax and abdomen

light wing tips

Male

Male - female in wheel position

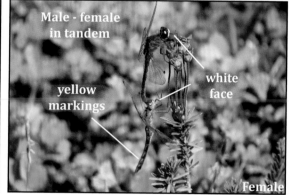

Male - female in tandem

yellow markings

white face

Female

Western Pondhawk

Erythemis collocata   **Percher**

Males and females of this species are strikingly different in color—the mature males are an intense, powder blue; females are bright green. Immature males are also green, like the females. In fact, Western Pondhawks are the only green dragonflies in our range. Western Pondhawks prefer to perch on bare ground, which leads to a useful rule of thumb: "Blue dragonfly on the ground = Male Western Pondhawk." Found on small lakes and ponds, Western Pondhawks specialize in preying on damselflies.

Male: Male bodies are uniformly blue in color, with the same blue color on both the abdomen and thorax. All four wings are clear, and the eyes are blue. The face is bright green, with a bold, dark horizontal stripe across it —like a "Groucho Marx" mustache. Young males are green, and turn blue from the tip of the abdomen forward, until only the face remains green.

Female: Females are a striking chartreuse green. An egg scoop can be seen projecting downward near the tip of the abdomen. With age, the abdomen develops black stripes along the top and sides.

Similar Species: No other species in our range is green, like the immature male and female Western Pondhawk. The male Blue Dasher has a white face, amber near the base of the wings, and a thorax with white side stripes. Blue Dashers don't perch on the ground.

Life size photo   Length = 1.6"

Male

Range

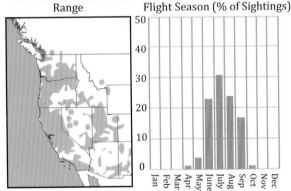

Flight Season (% of Sightings)

Immature male

Young male changing from green to blue

blue eyes

clear wings

uniformly blue body

Mature male

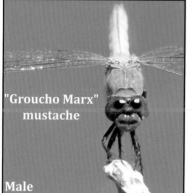

"Groucho Marx" mustache

Male

Female eating a damselfly

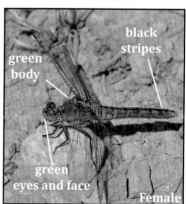

black stripes

green body

green eyes and face

Female

Variegated Meadowhawk

Sympetrum corruptum **Percher**

A truly unique and distinctive species, Variegated Meadowhawks are similar to other meadowhawks in their overall reddish color, but they are also completely different due to their complex (variegated) abdominal pattern. They are probably the most widespread of our dragonflies; it is possible to encounter a Variegated Meadowhawk in virtually any habitat at any time of the year. This is also one of the few dragonflies known to migrate. Pairs lay eggs in tandem, with the female repeatedly tapping the water.

Male: The abdominal pattern is unique, with "portholes"—white ovals bordered in black—along the sides. The thorax is brown with two white stripes on each side, and yellow spots at the lower end of the stripes. With age the white fades away, leaving only the yellow spots. The eyes vary from lavender to red above, and grayish below; stigmas are variegated (brown in the middle, yellow on either side); the face is red; wing veins are yellowish on the leading edge.

Female: Females have a pattern similar to males, but are more brownish to yellowish overall. The sides of the abdomen have a white stripe bordered in black above.

Similar Species: No other species has yellow spots on the sides of the thorax and a complex abdominal pattern with "portholes".

Life size photo — Length = 1.6"

Immature male

Range

Flight Season (% of Sightings)

Immature male

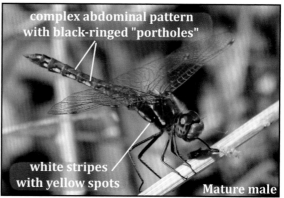

complex abdominal pattern with black-ringed "portholes"

white stripes with yellow spots

Mature male

Male - female in wheel position

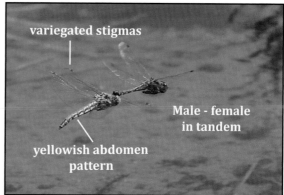

variegated stigmas

yellowish abdomen pattern

Male - female in tandem

Cardinal Meadowhawk

Sympetrum illotum   Percher

The Cardinal Meadowhawk is the most intensely red of all the dragonflies in our range. The red color is so brilliant, in fact, that it almost looks artificial, like a plastic toy. Once perched, which they do often, these dragonflies tend to fold their wings forward around the thorax as they scan the surroundings. They often elevate their brilliant red abdomens for greater visibility to females and potential rivals. Egg laying is done in tandem, near the shore of a small lake or pond.

Male: Males have a brilliant red abdomen that is wide, flat, and free of dark marks. The face and eyes are dark red, and each side of the thorax has two white spots—the remnants of white stripes in younger individuals. The best field mark is the dark red patch at the base of each wing. These patches are larger and more conspicuous in the hindwings.

Female: A reddish-brown version of the male. Each side of the thorax has two white spots, and the eyes are red. The wings have dark red patches at their base, similar to those on the male.

Similar Species: The Red-veined Meadowhawk has a darker red color, a cylindrical abdomen with small black spots, and reddish wing veins along the leading edge. The Flame Skimmer is larger and stockier, with reddish wing patches that go halfway to the tip.

Life size photo   Length = 1.5"

Male

Range

Flight Season (% of Sightings)

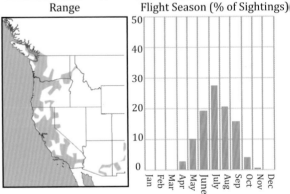

Male

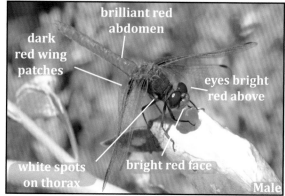

brilliant red abdomen

dark red wing patches

eyes bright red above

white spots on thorax

bright red face

Male

Pair laying eggs in tandem

Emerging egg

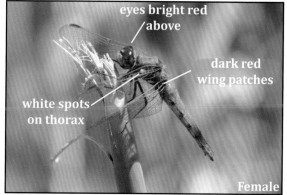

eyes bright red above

dark red wing patches

white spots on thorax

Female

DRAGONFLIES | 103

Red-veined Meadowhawk

Sympetrum madidum   **Percher**

A meadowhawk that can be locally common, though it is seldom seen at most meadowhawk locations. These dragonflies prefer the grassy margins of ditches and marshes. They lay eggs—generally in tandem, or with the male hovering nearby—by dropping them from midair into grassy areas that are dry in summer, but will be underwater when rains return in the fall. Their small yellow eggs, about the size of a grain of rice, can be seen bouncing off leaves after the female flicks them off the tip of her abdomen.

Male: A dark red meadowhawk with red eyes and face, small white stripes or spots on the sides of the thorax, and small dark markings near the tip of the cylindrical abdomen. Stripes on the sides of the thorax darken with age, leaving just white spots. The wings have a reddish color in the veins along the leading edge. There are also small, pale amber patches near the base of the wings.

Female: Females are similar to males, but more yellowish-red in color when young, and brownish-red when mature.

Similar Species: Cardinal Meadowhawks have dark red patches at the base of the wings, and no black on their flattened abdomens. Saffron-winged Meadowhawks have yellowish veins on the leading edge of the wings, and yellow stigmas with black borders fore and aft.

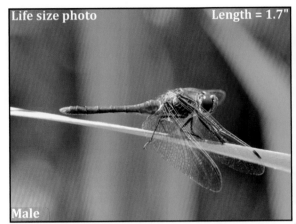

Life size photo   Length = 1.7"

Male

Range

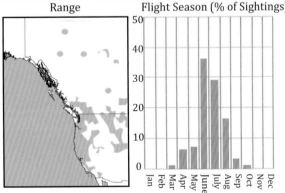

Flight Season (% of Sightings)

white spots

Male

black spots

red veins

red eyes and face

Male

Male

Male - female in tandem

red veins

white spots

White-faced Meadowhawk

Sympetrum obtrusum   **Percher**

A strikingly beautiful meadowhawk, with intense red on the body, black along the sides of the abdomen, and a brilliantly white face. This species, which is often found at high elevation, perches on shoreline vegetation of ponds and small lakes. It is easy to approach, and is a perfect subject for observation and photography. Eggs are generally laid in tandem, but sometimes with the male hovering nearby or perched on vegetation. The female sometimes drops eggs from a perch into shallow water or dry pond margins that flood later in the year.

Male: The male of the White-faced Meadowhawk is distinguished by its intensely white face, brownish-red thorax, and deep red abdomen with a jet black "saw-tooth" stripe along the sides. Wings are mostly clear, sometimes with a bit of amber near the base; eyes are bright red above, and grayish-green below. There may be a yellowish color along the leading edge of the wing.

Female: Females have the same white face as the male, but are yellowish-tan over most of the body. A black sawtooth stripe that is a bit wider than the male's is seen on the sides of the abdomen. The eyes are brownish-red above and yellowish-green below.

Similar Species: Cherry-faced Meadowhawks have a red face. Striped Meadowhawks have light stripes on the front and sides of the thorax.

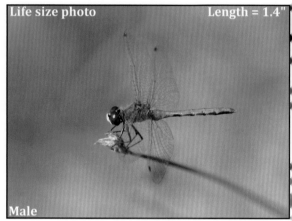

Life size photo   Length = 1.4"

Male

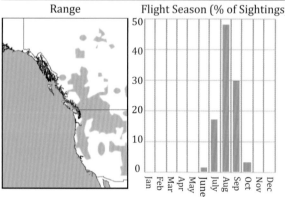

Range   Flight Season (% of Sightings)

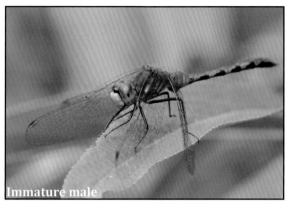

Immature male

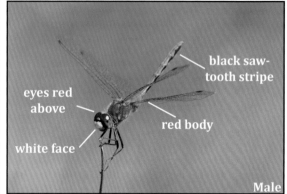

eyes red above

white face

black saw-tooth stripe

red body

Male

Male - female in wheel position

eyes reddish above

light tan face

yellowish body

black saw-tooth stripe

Female

Striped Meadowhawk

Sympetrum pallipes   **Percher**

This is a well-named meadowhawk, with lots of stripes on both the thorax and abdomen. The males are unique among other male meadowhawks in our range as they have tan faces. Tenerals of this species are bright yellow, turning red as they mature. Striped Meadowhawks lay eggs in small lakes, ponds and ditches. The female flicks the tip of her abdomen to release one or two bright yellow eggs at a time as she hovers. Sometimes the eggs land on dry ground, which will be covered with water later in the year. In some cases, eggs are deposited in inappropriate locations, such as sprinkled lawns. As the female lays eggs, the male may remain attached in tandem, guard from a nearby perch, or leave the female unattended.

Male: Males have a red abdomen, with a black "sawtooth" stripe running down the sides, and a red thorax with white stripes on the front and sides. The eyes have red dorsal fovea on top, and are tan to yellowish below. The wings are mostly clear, with a bit of amber near the base, and the stigma are two-toned—red in the middle and yellowish at either end.

Female: Similar in most respects to the male, but the black stripe on the side of the abdomen is straight, and bordered below by a light yellow stripe.

Similar Species: No other species in our range has so many stripes, and a tan face in the male.

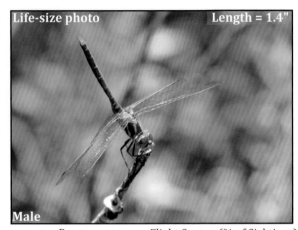

Life-size photo   Length = 1.4"

Male

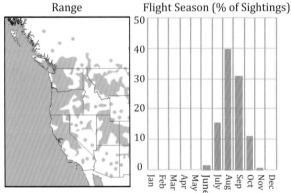

Range   Flight Season (% of Sightings)

two-toned stigma

Immature male raising abdomen in obelisk posture

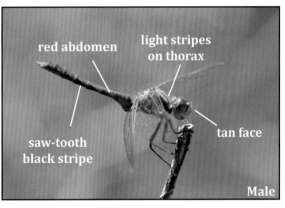

red abdomen

light stripes on thorax

saw-tooth black stripe

tan face

Male

Female laying eggs

Emerging egg

light stripes on thorax

straight black stripe

Female

Cherry-faced Meadowhawk

Sympetrum internum   **Percher**

A small, bright-red meadowhawk, found mostly at small lakes and beaver ponds, often at high elevation. Pairs spend considerable time flying in the wheel position and in tandem. Egg laying is generally done in tandem, though solo females also lay eggs. The eggs are dropped from a height of a couple feet onto bare ground that will become covered with water later in the year. Individuals perch on vegetation near the shore, or on the ground farther back from the water.

Male: Males have a bright "cherry-red" face. Their thorax is plain and reddish, the eyes are red, the legs are black, and the abdomen has a black saw-tooth stripe along its sides. The wings have amber washes near the base, and some reddish color in the veins. The face is yellowish red in young individuals, and turns darker red with age.

Female: Females are similar to males, but are yellowish to brownish-red in color. They have a thick black side stripe on the abdomen.

Similar Species: White-faced Meadowhawks have a white face. Saffron-winged Meadowhawks have stigmas that are yellow with black borders; they also have less black on the abdomen. Striped Meadowhawks have tan stripes on the thorax and tan faces. Cardinal Meadowhawks have white spots on the sides of the thorax and no black on the abdomen.

Life size photo   Length = 1.3"

Male

Range

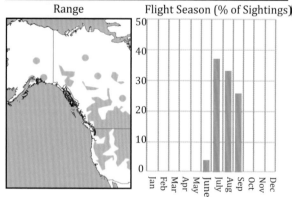

Flight Season (% of Sightings)

Male

solid red thorax

red eyes and face

black saw-tooth

Male

Male

overall brownish color

thick black side stripe

Female

Photo credit: Dennis Paulson

Saffron-winged Meadowhawk

Sympetrum costiferum Percher

A distinctive meadowhawk with yellow (saffron) veins along the leading edge of the wings. The Saffron-winged Meadowhawk is found in a wide variety of habitats, from small lakes to ponds, and from lowlands to higher elevations. It perches along the shore on logs, rocks, or stems of vegetation. Pairs oviposit in tandem, tapping the water to deposit eggs in water near the shore, or even on a damp shoreline.

Male: Both sexes of the Saffron-winged Meadowhawk are distinguished by the yellow veins along the leading edge of the wings. Otherwise, the wings are clear. The stigmas are red with black borders fore and aft, which are easy to spot with binoculars. The body is mostly red, with small dark spots near the tip of the abdomen. Eyes are red on top, yellow below, and the face is reddish tan.

Female: Females are similar to males, but with a more yellowish brown color. They have a black side stripe along the length of the abdomen, which becomes more apparent with age. A modest egg scoop is visible on the underside of the abdomen, near the tip.

Similar Species: Autumn Meadowhawks lack yellow on the leading edge of the wings. Red-veined Meadowhawks have a reddish color on the leading edge of the wings, and white spots on the sides of the thorax. Striped Meadowhawks have stripes on the thorax.

Life size photo Length = 1.3"

Male

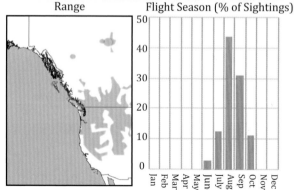

Range Flight Season (% of Sightings)

Male

saffron leading edge of wings

dark borders on stigmas

Male

Female laying eggs

saffron leading edge of wings

dark borders on stigmas

Female

Band-winged Meadowhawk

Sympetrum semicinctum   **Percher**

An attractive and distinctive meadowhawk whose large amber wing patches make for easy identification. This species often perches on the ground or other flat surfaces, such as a fallen tree trunk, but is also comfortable on small twigs and branches. Found mostly on small marshy lakes and ponds, the females lay eggs by tapping the water's surface as the pair flies in tandem.

Male: Large amber wing patches are the most obvious and distinctive feature of this dragonfly. Amber coloring extends from the base of the wings to the nodus; that is, about half the length of the wing. The patches are bold on the hindwings, but much paler on the forewings. The abdomen is red, with a black side stripe and black marks on the top of segments 8 and 9. Eyes are dark red on top (the dorsal fovea), and yellowish below. The thorax has yellow side stripes.

Female: Females are mostly yellow overall, with a paler version of the same amber wing patches found in the male. The abdomen is yellow with a black side stripe and black marks on top of segments 8 and 9. The thorax has light yellow side stripes, the dorsal fovea are red, and the lower eyes and face are yellow.

Similar Species: Band-winged Meadowhawks are the only meadowhawk in our range with large amber wing patches.

Life size photo   Length = 1.5"

Male

Range   Flight Season (% of Sightings)

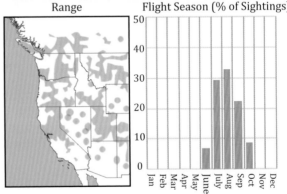

Immature male

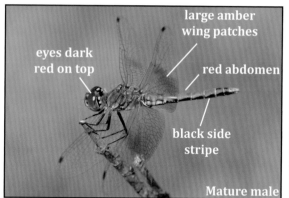

eyes dark red on top

large amber wing patches

red abdomen

black side stripe

Mature male

Female

yellow abdomen

pale amber wing patches

eyes red on top, yellow below

Female

Autumn Meadowhawk

Sympetrum vicinum **Percher**

A small, delicate dragonfly of lakes and ponds that have soggy vegetation along the shore. Despite its fragile appearance, this is a hardy species, with one of the latest flight seasons in our area—hence the common name. It is also our friendliest dragonfly. In fact, if a red dragonfly lands on you, chances are it's an Autumn Meadowhawk. This species lays eggs in tandem in a unique four-step process: (1) the pair hovers in tandem; (2) the female dips the tip of her abdomen into the water to collect a droplet on her "egg scoop"; (3) the pair hovers for about a second as the female lays eggs in the droplet; (4) the pair swoops downward, slamming the female's abdomen against stems and leaves, dislodging the egg-filled droplet into the moist vegetation on the shore. They repeat this procedure time after time, making it easy to observe.

Male: Males have few distinctive features, other than an overall reddish color, including on the face and eyes, and small amber patches near the base of the wings.

Female: Females have an overall brownish-red color. Their most distinctive feature is the large "egg scoop" protruding downward near the tip of the abdomen.

Similar Species: Striped Meadowhawks have a tan face, light thorax stripes, and black stripes on the abdomen. Cardinal Meadowhawks have red patches at the base of the wings, and white spots on the sides of the thorax.

Life size photo
Length = 1.3"
Male

Range

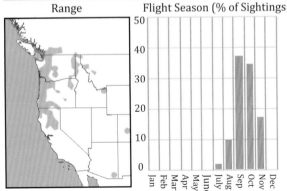

Flight Season (% of Sightings

Resting group

clear wings, amber near base

red eyes and face

red body

hamules

Male

Male - female in wheel position

clear wings, amber near base

red eyes and face

reddish-orange body

large egg scoop

Female

Black Meadowhawk

Sympetrum danae **Percher**

A distinctively small, dark, delicate dragonfly; very different from all other meadowhawks. Black Meadowhawks favor thickly vegetated margins of marshy bogs and ponds. Males perch in prominent locations, and are so small they can be mistaken for a spreadwing or other damselfly. They generally perch on logs and stems of vegetation, but are also found perched on dark ground, where they blend in and can be hard to spot. The species is wary, and sometimes hard to approach, but once you get close they are fairly tolerant of your presence.

Male: The body and eyes are brownish-black, and the wings are clear. Young males are dull yellow, like females, but quickly turn dark brown with age. They are often seen with rows of yellow spots on the abdomen, a holdover from their youth.

Female: Females are mostly yellow, turning more brownish with age. They have a complex brown-and-yellow pattern on the abdomen, and on the sides of the thorax, and an amber wash at the base of the wings. Their eyes are generally reddish above, on the dorsal fovea, and yellowish below.

Similar Species: All other male meadowhawks in our range have red in the body. All other female meadowhawks are larger, with a fairly heavy build.

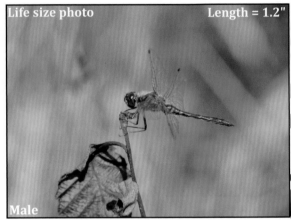

Life size photo   Length = 1.2"

Male

Range

Flight Season (% of Sightings

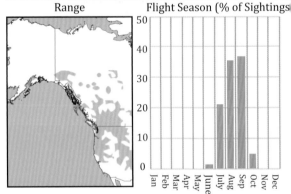

Male

clear wings

dark brown body

dark brown eyes

faint yellow spots

Male

Female

eyes reddish on top

Female

Blue Dasher

Pachydiplax longipennis   Percher

This is one of the most common, beautiful and wide-spread dragonflies in our range. Blue Dashers always perch above the ground, and spend most of their time on a favorite stem or leaf. They are easy to approach, and frequently strike delightfully photogenic poses. Males and females are completely different in this species—the males are a beautiful blue, the females are brown with lovely yellow stripes. Males perch along the shore of lakes and ponds facing the water, looking for rivals, prey, and mates.

Male: Males have a light-blue abdomen, darker-blue thorax with light stripes, bluish-green eyes, and a white face. A small amount of amber appears near the base of the wings. When a male looks directly at you, the dorsal fovea become two large pseudopupils, and turn almost entirely black. Young males look like females.

Female: Females have brown bodies with multiple yellow stripes along the edges of the abdomen and on the thorax. The eyes are red above and gray below.

Similar Species: Male Western Pondhawks have a bright green face, a light-blue thorax with no stripes, and clear wings. They perch on the ground if a bare patch is available. Thus a useful rule of thumb is "blue dragonfly on the ground = Western Pondhawk." No other species in our range has the color pattern of a female Blue Dasher.

Life size photo   Length = 1.7"

Male

Range

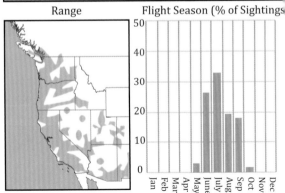

Flight Season (% of Sightings)

Male

light blue abdomen

blue-green eyes, white face

dark blue thorax with light stripes

Male

hamules

Male

dark body with bright yellow stripes

eyes red above, gray below

Female

Black Saddlebags

Tramea lacerata   **Flyer**

A large, black dragonfly easily identified in flight by distinctive wing patches (the "saddlebags") on its hindwings. A migratory species, it is found on lakes, ponds, marshes, and streams, where it glides frequently on its long, broad wings. When perched, these dragonflies often hang vertically like darners. As with all saddlebags, eggs are laid in an elaborate three-part process: (1) the pair hovers in tandem over a favorable spot for egg laying; (2) the male droops his hindwings downward quickly as a signal to the female, then releases her so she can drop to the water and deposit an egg; (3) the female rises and the male drops down until the couple reunites, attaches in tandem, and continues the process. Steps (2) and (3) happen very quickly, so watch closely to see this interesting behavior.

Male: The most conspicuous field marks of males are large black wing patches on the broad hindwings. The body, eyes, and face are black, though the abdomen has a yellow spot or two near segment 7, which darken and fade with age. The saddlebags are easily seen in flight.

Female: Similar to males, but with a brownish body, and more prominent yellow spots on the abdomen that grow in size near the tip of the abdomen.

Similar Species: No other species in our area is similar.

Life size photo   Length = 2.1"

Male

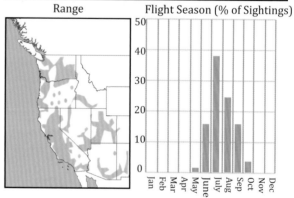

Range   Flight Season (% of Sightings)

"saddlebags" shading abdomen

Male

black abdomen with yellow spots

black "saddlebags"

Male

Photo credit: Pierre Deviche

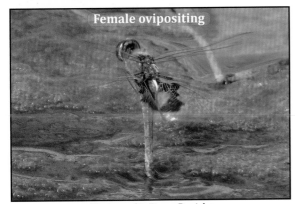

Female ovipositing

Photo credit: Pierre Deviche

dark brown body with yellow spots on abdomen

black "saddlebags"

Female

Photo credit: Pierre Deviche

Wandering Glider

Pantala flavescens   **Flyer**

A fascinating dragonfly that is known to migrate great distances—even across oceans. Its hindwings are much wider than in most dragonflies, extending almost half the length of the abdomen; this is an adaptation for efficient gliding on its long-range flights (*Pantala* means "all wings"). Wandering Gliders breed in temporary ponds, ditches, and freshly filled wetlands free of fish. They sometimes lay eggs in inappropriate places, such as the hoods of cars or on asphalt, apparently mistaking these surfaces for water. Females lay eggs by tapping the water either alone or guarded by the male.

Male: A useful nickname for this species is "Colonel Mustard," due to its mustard yellow face, which can be seen in flight. The body is light yellow, with the thorax a bit more brownish. On top of the abdomen is a dark stripe running down the middle, becoming more prominent toward the tip, and developing into distinct black spots on segments 8–10. This species has beautiful eyes that are deep red above and gray below, contrasting nicely with the mustard face. The large, expansive wings are clear, but with small amber spots near the tips.

Female: Females look very much like males.

Similar Species: Spot-winged Gliders are darker overall, with small dark patches on the hindwings along the sides of the abdomen.

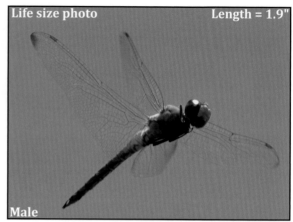

Life size photo   Length = 1.9"

Male

Range

Flight Season (% of Sightings)

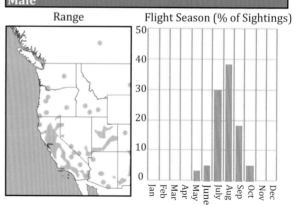

red eyes, yellow face

Male

clear wings

small amber spots

yellow body, black spots

Male

Male

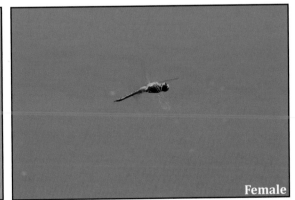

Female

Spot-winged Glider

Pantala hymenaea   **Flyer**

The Spot-winged Glider is a migratory species that favors newly filled wetlands and temporary pools free of fish. It can complete its development in less than a month, which is a great adaptation for life in such temporary waters. The hindwings are extremely wide, ideally suited to help this dragonfly glide and soar during long flights. Some reports suggest this species perches only at the end of the day, but in fact it perches off and on all day long. Watch for one to fly low and slow over sunlit bushes, and you will have a good chance of seeing it perch and "hang up" in a vertical position. Pairs lay eggs in tandem, with the female tapping the surface of the water to deposit small egg masses from the tip of her abdomen.

Male: Males have eyes that are red above and gray below; the face is dull red. The abdomen is brown overall, and more so with age, but with small white and black spots along the top of each segment. The hindwings are wide, with small distinctive dark spots on either side of the abdomen. These dark spots can be seen in flight, especially when an individual flies overhead.

Female: Females are very similar to males, though the eyes are more brownish, the face is lighter red, and the abdomen is darker brown.

Similar Species: Wandering Gliders are yellowish overall, with a mustard yellow face and clear wings.

Life size photo | Length = 1.9"
Male

Range

Flight Season (% of Sightings)

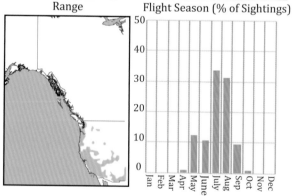

dark wing spots near abdomen

brownish spots along abdomen

Male

brownish abdomen

wide hind wings

Male

Female

Female

Identifying Mosaic Darners

Darners of the genera *Aeshna* and *Rhioaeschna* are referred to as mosaic darners, because the intricate patterns of spots on their abdomens are reminiscent of mosaic tiles. These darners are quite similar in appearance and can be a challenge to identify correctly. Paying attention to appendages, stripes, and spots on the abdomen can simplify the process.

Appendages

Male upper appendages (cerci) come in three types: simple, paddle-shaped, and forked. Females only have upper appendages, and they are always simple in shape. Below is a table of species, along with an illustration of each type of male appendage.

Simple (a)
California Darner
Canada Darner
Variable Darner

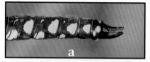

Paddle shaped (b)
Paddle-tailed Darner
Shadow Darner
Walker's Darner

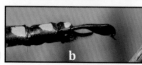

Forked (c)
Blue-eyed Darner

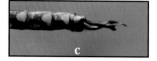

Thorax Stripes

Thorax stripes, both on the front and the sides of the thorax, can be a key identifying field mark. Examples are given below.

California Darner
No front stripes

Canada Darner
Notched side stripes

Variable Darner
Pinched-in side stripes

Shadow Darner
Black border on side stripes

Photo credit Dennis Paulson

Paddle-tailed Darner versus Shadow Darner

The Paddle-tailed Darner and the Shadow Darner are the two mosaic darners that are most alike. Key distinguishing features are the following: (1) the shape and color of the front stripes on the thorax; (2) the shape of the blue stripe on the top of segment 2 of the abdomen; (3) whether segment 10 of the abdomen is blue or black.

Paddle-tailed Darner

Shadow Darner

Paddle-tailed Darner

Yellowish front stripes pinched in at top

Shadow Darner

Greenish front stripes wide at top

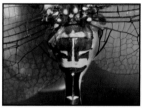

Segment 2 stripe straight

Segment 2 stripe spindle shaped

Segment 10 blue

Segment 10 black

The "Happy-face" Dragonfly

The discovery of the "Happy-face" Dragonfly was one of pure serendipity. I was trying out a new camera when I spotted a Paddle-tailed Darner in the bushes. I raised my camera, put it in front of the darner's face, and snapped a photo without even looking in the viewfinder. It wasn't until I got home and looked at the image on the computer that I discovered the Paddle-tailed Darner's remarkable face.

That epiphany marked the beginning of my wonderful odyssey into the world of dragonflies and damselflies which continues to this day.

The Many Faces of the "Happy-face" Dragonfly

I've taken lots of pictures of the "Happy-face" Dragonfly since that first one. Here are a number of other looks at the face of a Paddle-tailed Darner.

The Faces of Other Darners

Other species of darners have faces that are similar to the happy face of the Paddle-tailed Darner. A sampling is given to the right. Perhaps the closest are the Shadow and Variable Darners, both members of the same genus (*Aeshna*) as the Paddle-tailed Darner. The California and Blue-eyed Darners belong to a different genus (*Rhionaeschna*), and lack the eyebrows of the "Happy-face."

Shadow Darner

Variable Darner

Paddle-tailed Darner Full body view looking up at observer

California Darner

Blue-eyed Darner

River Jewelwing

Calopteryx aequabilis   **Percher**

The River Jewelwing is the largest and most spectacular damselfly in our range. The large black patches on the wings of the male, and the intense metallic iridescence in both sexes, are strikingly beautiful and unmistakable. Both sexes perch frequently on the shoreline vegetation of warm-water streams and rivers. Males open their wings slowly, to show off their black wing patches, and then flip them shut again. Their flight is fluttering, like a butterfly, and from a distance you see only the black patches bobbing up and down. Males drop down to touch the water's surface with their flapping wings in an attempt to entice females to mate.

Male: Large black wing patches covering the outer half of the wings are the most obvious field marks. The entire body is intensely iridescent, with a metallic green color when viewed from one direction, and a metallic blue color when viewed from another direction. The eyes and face are dark brown.

Female: Generally lacks the black wing patches of the male. Instead, its wings are tinted uniformly with an amber color. Stigmas are snow white, contrasting sharply with the rest of the wings. The body is intensely metallic green, and the eyes and face are dark brown.

Similar Species: No other species resembles the River Jewelwing in appearance.

Life size photo   Length = 1.9"

Male

Range   Flight Season (% of Sightings

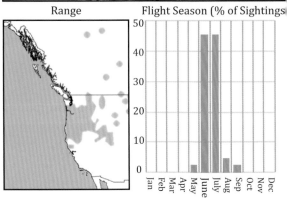

Male

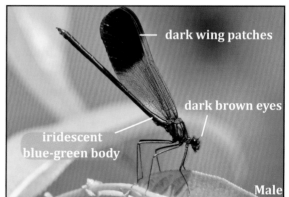

dark wing patches

dark brown eyes

iridescent
blue-green body

Male

Female

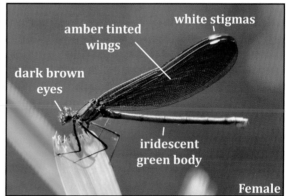

amber tinted
wings

white stigmas

dark brown
eyes

iridescent
green body

Female

DAMSELFLIES | 133

American Rubyspot

Hetaerina americana   **Percher**

A large, prominent damselfly with distinctive flame-red patches at the base of the wings. Males and females perch on vegetation along the shores of swift-running streams and rivers, and are often seen perching on mid-stream rocks. The red wing patches are conspicuous in perched individuals, and even more obvious in flight. The patches extend from the base of the wings to just short of the nodus. These damselflies are sometimes found in such large numbers that it can be hard to close the door of a car without trapping several inside. Males flash their wing patches to defend their territory, and also bend their abdomens forward with open appendages in a threat posture. Females lay eggs unattached to a male, and sometimes submerge completely during the process.

Male: Males have distinctive red wing patches with white veins. The head and eyes are dark red, and the thorax is a lustrous, metallic red. The abdomen is dark brown, with a reddish and/or greenish iridescence. The stigmas are small and inconspicuous.

Female: Reddish wing patches are distinctive in females as well. The thorax is a metallic reddish-brown, with cream-colored stripes on the side. The abdomen is reddish-brown above, and cream colored below.

Similar Species: No other damselfly in our range has red wing patches.

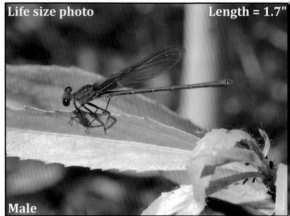

Life size photo   Length = 1.7"

Male

Range

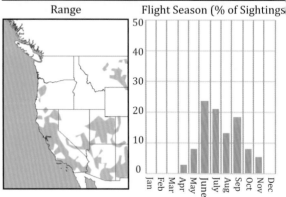

Flight Season (% of Sightings)

Male: threat display

red patch with white veins

reddish thorax

dark eyes

Male

brownish thorax with pale side stripes

Female

Male

some red in wings

ovipositor

Female

California Spreadwing

Archilestes californicus **Percher**

The California Spreadwing is the largest spreadwing in our range. It's so large, in fact, that in flight it sometimes looks like a meadowhawk. California Spreadwings often perch at eye level, and are easy to approach for photographs. They are found on small, slow-moving streams, as well as on the shores of ponds and lakes. Pairs lay eggs in tandem in the vertical stems of bushes and small trees. They sometimes lay eggs far from the shoreline, and at shoulder height above the ground. When the larvae hatch, they have a long way to go to reach the nearest water.

Male: Unmistakably large spreadwing. The body is mostly brown, with brown and black stripes on the front of the thorax, and a distinctive light stripe on the side of the thorax with black borders fore and aft. The abdomen is brown, with light rings at the base of each segment and a pruinose tan tip. Stigmas are light tan, and the eyes are blue.

Female: Mostly brown overall, but with the same light stripe bordered by black stripes on the side of the thorax. The eyes are light brown, and the tip of the abdomen has a prominent bulge containing the ovipositor.

Similar Species: The Spotted Spreadwing has a "staircase" pattern on the side of the thorax, and a pruinose blue tip on the abdomen.

Life size photo — Length = 2.0"

Male

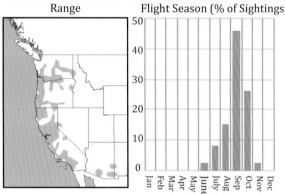

Range

Flight Season (% of Sightings)

Male

blue eyes

pale stripe with dark borders

pale rings on abdomen

Male

Female

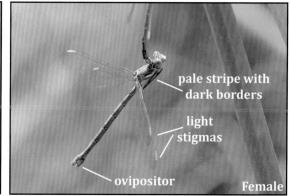

pale stripe with dark borders

light stigmas

ovipositor

Female

Spotted Spreadwing

Lestes congener   Percher

These large damselflies are frequently seen in much of our range. The spots referred to in the common name are dark spots on the underside of the thorax, and are not generally seen. As with other spreadwings, the wings are held out at a 45° angle to the body when perched. Found on lakes, ponds, and ditches, this species is often seen flying in tandem as they go about the business of laying eggs. The female probes the stem of a plant, cuts a slit in it with her ovipositor, and deposits eggs in the slit. In general, the eggs are laid on stems above dry ground, but in an area that will be submerged later in the year.

Male: The key identifying feature for this species is the "staircase" pattern of light-colored, rectangular bars on the sides of the thorax. In addition, the front of the thorax is dark. The abdomen is dark over most of its length, but has a powder blue tip. Spotted Spreadwings have eyes that are a lovely shade of blue—well worth making an effort to see.

Female: Females are brown in color, including the eyes, though they have the same "staircase" pattern on the sides of the thorax as the male. The abdomen is brown, with a noticeably enlarged tip where the ovipositor is housed.

Similar Species: Northern Spreadwings are similar in appearance, but their thorax is overall pruinose blue, with subtle blue side stripes.

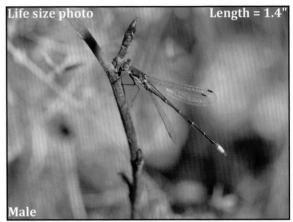

Life size photo   Length = 1.4"

Male

Range   Flight Season (% of Sightings)

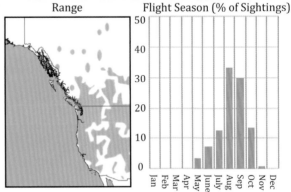

Male

staircase pattern

pruinose blue tip

hamules

Male

Female

staircase pattern

ovipositor

Male - Female

Northern Spreadwing

Lestes disjunctus   **Percher**

A spreadwing damselfly distinguished by its prominent pruinosity (dusty appearance). Found on shoreline vegetation of lakes, ponds, and marshes, these spreadwings sally forth to snap up small passing insects, and then return to their perch. Pairs mating in the wheel position can stay connected for up to 15 minutes. They generally remain attached in tandem as the female cuts a slit in the stem of a bulrush or other emergent vegetation with her ovipositor. Once the slit is cut, she lays a small group of eggs inside the stem. The pair then moves to another stem to repeat the process.

Male: Males have blue pruinosity on most of the thorax, and at the base and tip of the abdomen. A dark shoulder stripe on either side of the thorax remains even when the front of the thorax has become totally pruinose. The eyes are a beautiful blue, and the stigmas are uniformly dark.

Female: Females have eyes that can vary from brownish to bluish. They also have a pale stripe on the shoulders of the brownish thorax, and sometimes show pruinosity at the base and tip of the abdomen. The tip of their abdomen is enlarged due to the presence of an ovipositor.

Similar Species: Spotted Spreadwings have a dark front to the thorax, with no pruinosity, and a staircase pattern on the sides. Lyre-tipped Spreadwings have stigmas that are dark in the middle and light at either end.

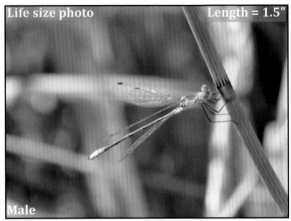

Life size photo   Length = 1.5"

Male

Range

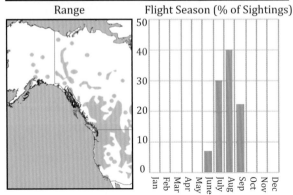

Flight Season (% of Sightings)

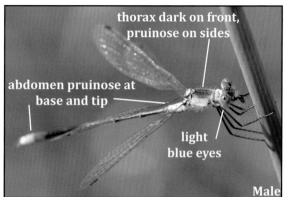

thorax dark on front, pruinose on sides

abdomen pruinose at base and tip

light blue eyes

Male

Male

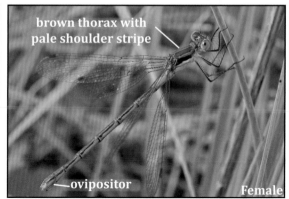

Male

brown thorax with pale shoulder stripe

—ovipositor

Female

Photo credit: Pierre Deviche

Photo credit: Pierre Deviche

DAMSELFLIES | 141

Lyre-tipped Spreadwing

Lestes unguiculatus   **Percher**

This damselfly owes its common name to its distinctive "lyre-shaped" appendages. It spends much of its time perched on shoreline vegetation or long grass. Mating in the wheel position occurs for extended periods of time, and once mating is complete, the egg-laying process stretches on for an hour or more. To lay eggs, the pair lands on a stem of emergent vegetation, where the female probes with her ovipositor, cuts a slit, and deposits eggs. The eggs are often laid where the surface is dry in the summer, but flooded later in the year.

Male: Males have a thorax that is metallic brown, with light blue shoulder stripes, and pale or whitish pruinosity low on the sides. The abdomen is metallic dark green above and pale blue below. The stigmas are distinctly two-toned—dark in the middle, and cream colored at either end—which is a useful field mark. In addition, the famous appendages have a curved "lyre" shape that is easily seen in binoculars.

Female: Females are similar to males, but with darker and broader stripes on the thorax. The abdomen is dark above and pale cream below, and the tip is enlarged with the ovipositor mechanism.

Similar Species: Spotted Spreadwings have a staircase pattern on the sides of the thorax. Northern and Emerald Spreadwings have solid stigmas.

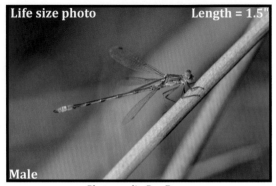

Life size photo   Length = 1.5"

Male

Photo credit: Ray Bruun

Range   Flight Season (% of Sightings)

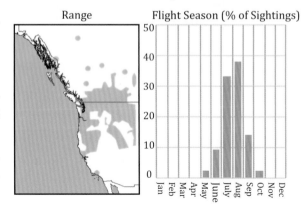

two-toned stigma

Male

abdomen metallic green above

pale blue tip

Male

lyre-shaped appendages

Female

abdomen dark above, pale cream below

ovipositor

Female

Photo credit (all photos): Ray Bruun

Emerald Spreadwing

Lestes dryas   Percher

A stocky spreadwing with a distinctive emerald green color on the thorax and abdomen. This species prefers fishless waters, and is often found in dense shoreline vegetation around ponds that dry up in the summer. Females oviposit in stems or leaves of vegetation, frequently over areas that are currently dry, but will be flooded later in the year. They spend a sizable portion of their time perched, and often move just a few feet when disturbed.

Male: Males have an iridescent metallic green color on the front of the thorax and the top of the abdomen. The thorax has a thin light-colored shoulder stripe, and is pruinose white on the sides. The abdomen is metallic green above and cream colored on the underside, with some pruinosity at the base and the tip. The eyes are blue, and the stigmas are dark in the middle with thin cream borders on either end.

Female: Females are a similar metallic green on the thorax and abdomen, but duller in color. They have a more pronounced, thicker cream-colored stripe on the shoulder—although this is sometimes absent. The abdomen is green above, cream below, and lacks the pruinosity seen in males. At the tip, the abdomen is expanded to accommodate a rather large ovipositor.

Similar Species: Spotted Spreadwings have a thorax that is dark in front, with no iridescent green.

Life size photo   Length = 1.4"

Male

Range

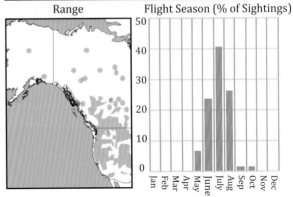

Flight Season (% of Sightings)

Male

blue eyes

pruinosity

iridescent green

Male

Male

brown eyes

iridescent green

ovipositor

Female

Familiar Bluet

Enallagma civile   **Percher**

A conspicuous and abundant resident of a variety of habitats, ranging from temporary pools, to marshes, ponds and lakes, to streams and rivers. Pairs mate for extended periods of time, and then lay eggs in tandem in stems of shoreline vegetation. Females often back down a stem until they are completely submerged. The male remains attached in tandem until the water rises to his thorax, at which point he disconnects and either hovers or perches on a nearby stem to wait for the female to resurface.

Male: The abdomen of this species is mostly blue, with black rings on segments 3-5. Segments 6 and 7 are mostly black on top, segments 8 and 9 are completely blue, and segment 10 is black on top. The appendages are prominent, giving a "forked" appearance to the tip of the abdomen. Segment 2 has a black spot on top that merges with segment 3. The thorax is mostly blue, with a wide black stripe on the front and a thin black stripe on the sides. The eyes are black on top, blue below.

Female: Females are tan or blue in color with the same pattern of stripes on the thorax as males. The abdomen is black above and light below, and expanded at the tip to contain an ovipositor.

Similar Species: Northern and Boreal Bluets have smaller black spots on the top of segment 2. Tule Bluets have more black than blue on the abdomen.

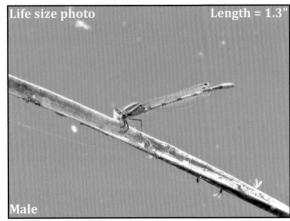

Life size photo   Length = 1.3"

Male

Range

Flight Season (% of Sightings)

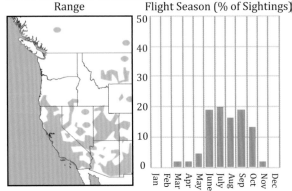

Male

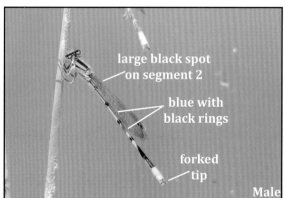

large black spot on segment 2

blue with black rings

forked tip

Male

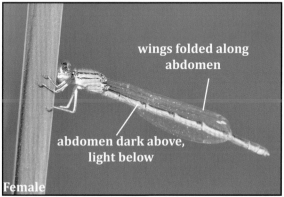

wings folded along abdomen

abdomen dark above, light below

Female

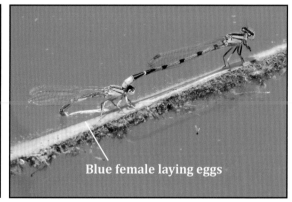

Blue female laying eggs

Tule Bluet

Enallagma carunculatum   Percher

Like other bluets, Tule Bluets are aggressive in defending their territory—they will often harass other damselflies, and even large dragonflies. Tule Bluet females land on vegetation along the shore of small lakes and ponds, and use their ovipositor to cut a slit in a stem and deposit eggs inside. Sometimes, a tandem pair slowly backs down a stem until the female is completely submerged. The male may stay attached and go underwater with the female; more often, he releases his grip when partly submerged, and hovers until the female reemerges. Sometimes a female is seen with the abdomen of a male still attached to her thorax—the result of an attack by a darner, which has grabbed a tandem pair and snipped off the male's thorax for a snack.

Male: Males have blue stripes on the thorax, a blue tip at the end of the abdomen, and alternating black and blue bands of roughly equal width (with the black bands slightly larger) on the middle segments of the abdomen.

Female: Females are generally greenish brown, though blue color forms are also observed. The thorax pattern is the same as in the male, and the abdomen is black on top with pale rings at the base of middle segments.

Similar Species: Northern and Boreal Bluets have wide bands of blue on their abdomens, with small black rings separating them.

Life size photo   Length = 1.2"

Male

Range

Flight Season (% of Sightings)

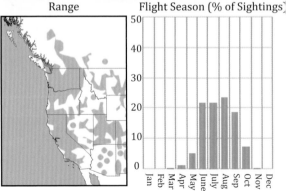

wings folded along abdomen

Male

black and blue bands, black wider than blue

Male

Male - female in wheel position

Male- female in wheel position

brownish-green thorax

Northern Bluet / Boreal Bluet

Enallagma annexum/Enallagma boreale　　**Percher**

Hardy and aggressive damselflies of small lakes and ponds, Northern and Boreal Bluets are sometimes seen in groups so large the grass along the shoreline looks blue, and each step you take flushes a bluish cloud of individuals. These species spend considerable time mating, as well as in tandem during egg laying. Eggs are generally placed on floating vegetation, though females may submerge for as long as 90 minutes to lay eggs underwater. They are flighty, and difficult to approach, and vigorously attack and harass other damselflies and dragonflies in their territory.

Male: These damselflies typify the mnemonic "lots of blue in it = bluet." They have more blue than black in the abdomen, with segments 3-5 mostly blue, segments 6, 7, and 10 mostly black, and segments 8 and 9 all blue. The appendages at the tip of the abdomen are small and inconspicuous—and the only reliable way to distinguish between these species. Segment 2 has a tiny black spot on top. The thorax is mostly blue, with a wide black stripe in front, and a thin black stripe on each side.

Female: Females can be brownish or bluish. They are similar to males in most respects, but with more black on the abdomen.

Similar Species: Familiar Bluets have large black spots on the top of segment 2 that merge with segment 3. They also have prominent "forked" appendages.

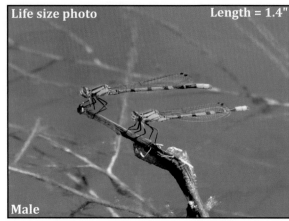

Life size photo　　Length = 1.4"

Male

Range

Flight Season (% of Sightings)

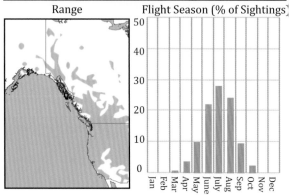

wings folded along abdomen

Male

more blue than black in abdomen

Male

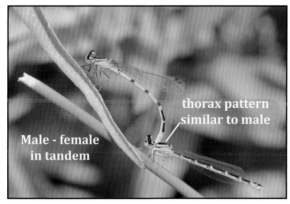

thorax pattern similar to male

Male - female in tandem

blue rings on top of abdomen

Female

Swift Forktail

Ischnura erratica   Percher

The Swift Forktail is the largest forktail in our range. It is found on small lakes and ponds, as well as slow-moving streams, where it perches on shoreline vegetation, rocks, and lily pads. Males display from their perches by raising the bright blue tip of their abdomen. Females lay eggs on the stems of shoreline vegetation, or submerge to lay their eggs underwater.

Male: This species has the typical forktail color pattern, as expressed by the mnemonic "blue only at the tip of the tail = forktail." It has two prominent spikes pointing backward from the tip of its tail, producing a literal "forktail." The thorax has straight blue shoulder stripes and blue on the sides. The abdomen is black on top, yellowish below, with light rings at the junctures between segments. At the tip, segment 7 is mostly blue on top, and segments 8 and 9 are completely blue on top. Segments 7-10 are black on the sides. The eyes are black above, and green below.

Female: Females start off a beautiful orange color, turning greenish as they mature. Their abdomens are all black above and yellow below. Females lack the forks at the tip of the tail, but instead have a bulge containing the ovipositor.

Similar Species: Western Forktails have green on the thorax. Pacific Forktails have spots rather than shoulder strips on the thorax.

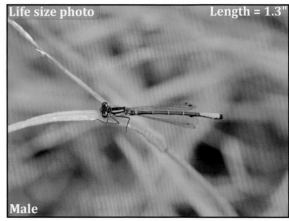

Life size photo   Length = 1.3"

Male

Range   Flight Season (% of Sightings)

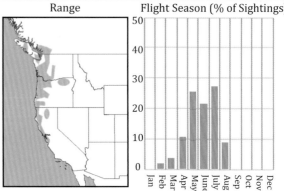

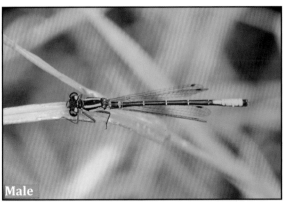

Male

black and blue on thorax

lots of blue at the tip

prominent forks

Male

Immature female

Male - female in wheel position

green on thorax

abdomen dark above, yellowish below

Pacific Forktail

Ischnura cervula   Percher

Widespread and common, the Pacific Forktail is one of the smallest, cutest, and "friendliest" damselflies in our range. It is more likely than any other to land on you as you stand on the shore of a small lake or pond, and it is easy to approach for photographs. Both males and females are easy to identify. As with all forktails, the abdomen is mostly dark, with a blue tip, leading to the following mnemonic: "blue only at the tip of the tail = forktail." This is in contrast to the abdomen of a bluet, which has lots of blue in it.

Male: A set of four blue spots on top of the thorax give a positive identification. The abdomen is black on the upper surface until the tip, where segments 8 and 9 are blue. The face and eyes are dramatic and cute, with the upper portion black, and the lower portion green.

Female: Gynomorphic (female form) females are tan to light lavender on the thorax, with reddish-brown eyes, and light tan stigmas. Andromorphic (male form) females have a blue thorax with stripes similar to those on bluets. Sometimes the upper stripes on the thorax pinch off in the middle, giving them an "exclamation point" shape. The tip of the abdomen has only a single blue segment (8), as opposed to two blue segments (8, 9) in the male.

Similar Species: The Western Forktail has a green thorax, with stripes on the front.

Life size photo   Length = 1.1"

Male

Range   Flight Season (% of Sightings)

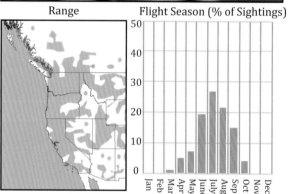

four blue spots on top of thorax

black and green face

Male

blue spots

mostly black abdomen with blue tip

Male

pinched-in stripes

blue thorax

Andromorphic female

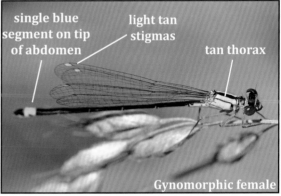

single blue segment on tip of abdomen

light tan stigmas

tan thorax

Gynomorphic female

Western Forktail

Ischnura perparva   Percher

The smallest damselfly in our range, the Western Forktail has the typical abdomen of a forktail—"blue only at the the tip of the tail = forktail." This species is unusual, however, in that males are seen infrequently, whereas females are common. In fact, it's thought that females mate just once, and retain the sperm from that mating to fertilize all the eggs they lay. As a result, mated females fend off advances from late-coming males. Eggs are laid without an accompanying male in stems along the shores of small lakes and ponds. Females, which are pruinose blue, look completely different from males.

Male: Males have a green-and-black thorax, with green shoulder stripes and mostly green sides. The abdomen is black above, yellowish below, with small light rings separating the middle segments. Segments 8 and 9 are blue, with black notches extending backward on the sides. The eyes are black on top and green below.

Female: Females have an orange color when young, but quickly become uniformly pruinose blue on both the thorax and abdomen—giving them the appearance of wearing blue pajamas. Their eyes are black above and green below.

Similar Species: Pacific Forktails have a blue-and-black thorax, with four blue spots on the shoulders. Swift Forktails have more blue on the tip of the abdomen.

Life size photo   Length = 1.0"
Immature female

Range

Flight Season (% of Sightings)

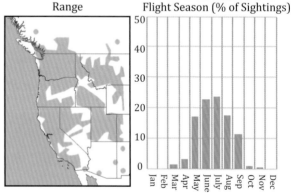

Immature female

black and green thorax

pale rings

blue tip on abdomen

Male

Female laying eggs

eyes black above, green below

body uniform pruinose blue

Mature female

Western Red Damsel

Amphiagrion abbreviatum   Percher

The only red damselfly in the northern part of our range, the Western Red Damsel is often hard to spot because of its small size and tendency to fly low to the ground and perch in thick grass. They are sometimes quite numerous, and will flush out of the grass in significant numbers as you walk through an area. Even so, they are not as frequently seen as their range might suggest. They are found in small ponds, ditches, and bogs, sometimes at high elevation. Pairs lay eggs in tandem, with the female probing submerged vegetation with her ovipositor.

Male: Males are distinguished by a dark red abdomen with black patches that grow larger near the tip. In some individuals, the abdomen is mostly red on the half near the thorax, and mostly black on the half near the tip. The thorax is black on top, and tannish-orange low on the sides. Eyes are generally dark red, with prominent horizontal stripes.

Female: The thorax of the female is tannish-red to orange. The abdomen varies from orange to a light shade of red, with an ovipositor that is quite prominent. Eyes are light brownish red, with distinct horizontal stripes.

Similar Species: The Desert Firetail is more slender, with a lighter red color, and no black on the abdomen.

Life size photo   Length = 1.0"

Male

Range

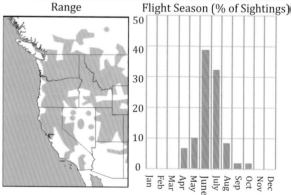

Flight Season (% of Sightings)

Immature male

thorax black on top

increasing black near tip

abdomen red near base

Mature male

Female - male in tandem

ovipositor

light red abdomen

Female

Desert Firetail

Telebasis salva   Percher

As its name suggests, this slender, delicate damselfly has an intense fiery red color, from its eyes to the tip of its abdomen. It is generally found on floating vegetation or shoreline bushes of ponds, lakes, and slow-moving streams. Mating in the wheel position lasts for an extended period of time. Pairs lay eggs in tandem, with the male firmly attached to the female and standing upright in a vertical position as she probes underwater for favorable laying sites with the tip of her abdomen. The pair moves from location to location, staying attached in tandem for as much as half an hour. Several pairs may lay eggs in close proximity, producing a group of vertical males that look like red blades of grass.

Male: Males have an intense red color over most of their body. They also have a dull black stripe down the front of the thorax, and on the back of the head between the eyes. The abdomen is solid red, and rather long, extending well beyond the wing tips. This species folds its wings along the abdomen when perched, like a bluet.

Female: Females have the same pattern of markings on the thorax and back of the head as the males, but are a duller yellowish-red to brownish-red in overall color.

Similar Species: Western Red Damsels are stockier, and also have extensive areas of black near the tip of the abdomen.

Life size photo   Length = 1.0"

Males

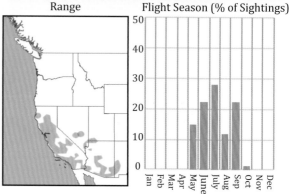

Range   Flight Season (% of Sightings)

Male - female in tandem

red body

dark stripes on thorax

red eyes

Male

Egg-laying pairs

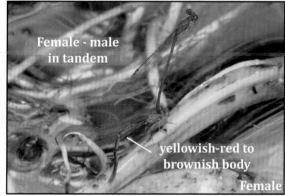

Female - male in tandem

yellowish-red to brownish body

Female

Vivid Dancer

Argia vivida   Percher

A large violet-blue, intensely-colored damselfly, with distinctive black markings on the thorax and abdomen. Vivid Dancers often perch on the ground, or on rocks in a stream. As with other dancers, they hold their wings high above the abdomen when perched. Pairs spend considerable time in the wheel position when mating. They lay eggs, usually in tandem, in the stems of shoreline vegetation. This is a widespread species, found at high elevation on vegetated streams, as well as in cities where you might see one perched at a pool or an outdoor café.

Male: Males have an intense blue to violet color that well deserves the term "vivid" in its common name. The front of the thorax has a broad black stripe down the center. Black stripes on the sides of the thorax are relatively wide at either end, and extremely thin in the middle. Black rings separate the blue on the middle segments of the abdomen, segment 7 is mostly black, and segments 8–10 are bright blue. Rear-pointing "arrowheads" are seen on the sides of segments 3-6.

Female: Females are a brownish version of the males, with the same basic pattern of markings. Some females are colored like males, but with a paler blue color.

Similar Species: Emma's Dancer has a lavender color, and lacks the arrowhead markings on the sides of the abdomen.

Life size photo · Length = 1.3"
Male

Range

Flight Season (% of Sightings)

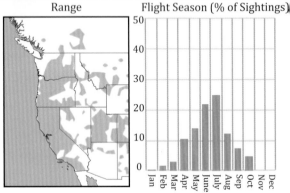

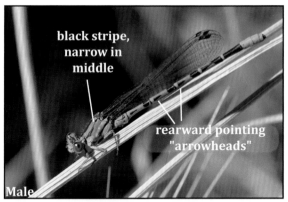

black stripe, narrow in middle

rearward pointing "arrowheads"

Male

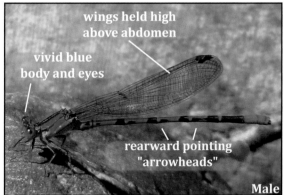

wings held high above abdomen

vivid blue body and eyes

rearward pointing "arrowheads"

Male

Male - female in tandem

tan body and eyes

same body pattern as male

Female

Emma's Dancer

Argia emma   **Percher**

The males of this lovely damselfly have a distinctive lavender color that sets them apart from all other species in our range. Both sexes perch with their wings held well above the abdomen, as is typical of dancers. Preferred egg-laying sites include floating vegetation, roots, and stems of emergent plants. It's not uncommon to see many pairs laying eggs in a tight group, with the males attached behind the head of the female, standing vertically upright like a group of exclamation points. Tandem pairs can be found resting together in bushes far from the shore of their preferred habitat of rocky streams and rivers.

Male: Males are easily identified, due to their overall lavender color. They also have a thin black stripe on the front of the thorax, and indented black stripes on the sides of the thorax. Narrow black rings separate the lavender on segments 3 – 5 of the abdomen; segments 6 and 7 are mostly black; segments 8 and 9 are bright blue. Some blue is generally seen on the top of segment 10.

Female: The lavender color of males is replaced with brown in females, though the thoracic and abdominal patterns of black markings are the same in both sexes.

Similar Species: No other species has the lavender color of the male. Vivid Dancers have a brilliant blue color, and black arrowhead marks on the sides of the abdomen.

Life size photo   Length = 1.4"

Male

Range   Flight Season (% of Sightings)

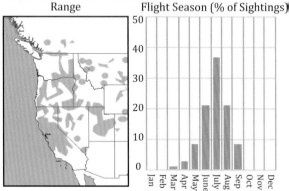

Male

wings held
above abdomen

blue tip
on abdomen

lavender
thorax

Male

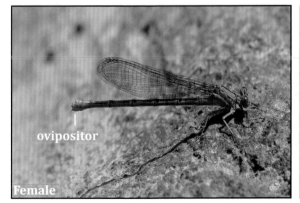

ovipositor

Female

wings held
above abdomen

tannish-brown
body color

Female

Identifying Spreadwings

Spreadwings are large damselflies that spread their wings outward at a 45 degree angle when perched. They are slender, and have small, well-separated eyes. They often have a favorite feeding perch from which they make short excursions to hunt prey, and then return to consume their catch.

A Distinctive Spreadwing

The Emerald Spreadwing is one of the easiest of the spreadwing species to identify. Its brilliant, metallic-green iridescence is unique among spreadwings in our range.

Emerald Spreadwing

Thorax Side Stripes

The other spreadwings in our range can be identified by the side stripes on the thorax, or by the lack of side stripes. Comparisons are shown below.

Spotted Spreadwing
"Staircase" side stripes

California Spreadwing
Light stripe with black border

Northern Spreadwing
Pruinose sides

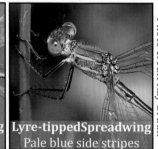
Lyre-tippedSpreadwing
Pale blue side stripes

Photo credit Ray Bruun

Identifying Bluets and Forktails

Bluets have a lot of blue in them, while forktails have blue mainly at the tail end of the abdomen. A comparison of the three male bluets and three male forktails in our range is shown on the right.

Female bluets are brownish in color, but female forktails can have rather striking colors. A few examples of female forktails are shown below.

Northern/Boreal Bluet

Tule Bluet

Pacific Forktail

Familiar Bluet

Pacific Forktail

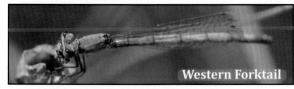

Western Forktail

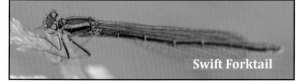

Swift Forktail

Western Forktail

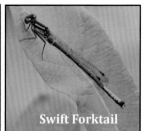

Swift Forktail

Further Information

A number of books and websites are available with additional information on odonates.

Books

Dragonflies and Damselflies of the West, by Dennis Paulson, Princeton University Press, Princeton, New Jersey, 2009. An extensive and comprehensive guide to odonates west of the Mississippi River.

Dragonflies and Damselflies of Oregon: A Field Guide, by Cary Kerst and Steve Gordon, Oregon State University Press, Corvallis, Oregon, 2011. A guide focused on odonates found in Oregon.

Common Dragonflies of California: A Beginner's Pocket Guide, by Kathy Biggs, Azalea Creek Publishing, Sebastopol, California, 2009. A brief odonate field guide for California.

Dragonflies: Behavior and Ecology of Odonata, by Philip Corbet, Ithaca, New York: Cornell University Press, 1999. A highly technical overview of odonates and their behavior.

A Dazzle of Dragonflies, by Forrest L. Mitchell and James L. Lasswell, Texas A&M University Press, Stephenville, Texas, 2005. A coffee-table book celebrating dragonflies and their diversity.

Websites

Odonata Central, http://www.odonatacentral.org. The official website of the Dragonfly Society of the Americas.

Arizona Dragonflies, http://azdragonfly.org. An excellent site covering the dragonflies and damselflies of Arizona, many of which are also found along the Pacific Coast.

The Dragonfly Whisperer, http://thedragonflywhisperer.blogspot.com. An informal blog of dragonfly experiences and general information by the author of this book.

Glossary

abdomen: The last major segment of the body, often referred to as the "tail," divided into 10 segments. The abdomen produces sperm in males and eggs in females.

andromorphic: A less typical color form in which a female dragonfly or damselfly has the same colors as a male.

anisoptera: The group of animals known as dragonflies. The term refers to the fact that the forewings are different from the hindwings.

appendages: The projections that extend beyond the tip of the abdomen. The appendages are used by the male to hold onto the female when in tandem, during mating, and while laying eggs.

cercus (*plural* cerci): The top two appendages on both dragonflies and damselflies.

compound eye: An eye comprised of thousands of individual eyes referred to collectively as ommatidia.

costa: The leading edge of a wing.

dorsal: The top or upper surface.

egg scoop: A colloquial term for the "flange" or "scoop" that extends downward beneath segment 8 of female dragonflies in families that include skimmers and meadowhawks. Eggs exit the body here.

epiproct: The single lower appendage on male dragonflies. The epiproct grips the front of the female's head when the two are connected to one another.

exuvia (*plural* exuviae): The shed larval skin when a dragonfly or damselfly emerges as an adult.

flight season: The time of year when adults are active.

fovea: The part of the eye with the sharpest vision.

gynomorphic: The more typical color form of a female dragonfly or damselfly, in which the colors are different from those of the male.

hamules: Paired structures that extend downward under segment 2 of male dragonflies and damselflies. The hamules are used to connect the abdomen of the male to that of the female.

head: The first segment of the body, containing the eyes and mouth.

immature: A term for an adult that is past the teneral stage, but still not fully mature, usually indicated by coloration that is fainter or a different color than that of mature adults. Often found away from the water.

larva (*plural* larvae): The immature form of dragonflies and damselflies after hatching from the egg. Typically aquatic.

mature: The term for an adult dragonfly or damselfly of breeding age.

nodus: The "bend" in the leading edge of the wings, approximately halfway from the base to the tip.

obelisk: A posture assumed by some dragonflies in which the abdomen is raised and pointed toward the sun to reduce body temperature.

odonata (*singular* **odonate**): The group of animals known as dragonflies and damselflies.

ommatidium (*plural* **ommatidia**): The individual eye in a compound eye.

ovipositor: The egg-laying structure, which produces a noticeable enlargement or "bulge" at the tip of the abdomen. Present in all female damselflies, as well as in female dragonflies of the darner and petaltail families.

paraprocts: The two lower appendages on male damselflies.

pruinosity: The white or light blue wax-like covering on the bodies of some mature dragonflies and damselflies.

pseudopupil: A dark spot on the compound eye of a dragonfly or damselfly that looks like the pupil of a vertebrate's eye. The pseudopupil follows the motion of an observer.

pterostigma: A dark—or sometimes white—mark along the leading edge of a dragonfly or damselfly wing near the tip.

range: The geographical extent of breeding locations of a particular species.

rhabdom: The light-absorbing structure in each ommatidium of a compound eye, similar in function to the retina of a vertebrate eye.

stigma: The mark on the leading edge of the wing near the tip. An abbreviation for the term pterostigma.

tandem: The term for a pair of dragonflies or damselflies that are physically connected, but not mating or laying eggs.

teneral: A dragonfly or damselfly that is freshly emerged from its larval skin. Tenerals are generally characterized by light vivid colors and flimsy cellophane-like wings.

thorax: The center segment of the body. The thorax contains the muscles that power the wings and legs.

tubercle: A bump or protrusion. Female Blue-eyed Darners have a tubercle under segment 2 of the abdomen.

wheel position: The mating position for all dragonflies and damselflies, in which the tip of the male's abdomen grips the female, and the tip of the female's abdomen attaches to the base of the male's abdomen. Only odonates mate in the wheel position.

zygoptera: The group of animals known as damselflies. The term refers to the fact that the forewings and hindwings are similar.

Acknowledgements

I must start with many loving thanks to my wonderful wife Betsy, who has shared my passion for dragonflies and damselflies, and has helped with many field trips and presentations over the years. We've had a great time exploring nature together.

I would also like to give special thanks to Dennis Paulson, who has been a mentor in my development as a dragonfly enthusiast, and who has always been more than generous with his time and expertise.

Pierre Deviche has also been very helpful and supportive in many ways, including through his wonderfully informative website on Arizona dragonflies—http://azdragonfly.org.

Thanks are also due to the many people who have attended my field trips and presentations, and especially Jan and Keith Wiggers, Tim Manns and Brenda Cunningham, Ron and Shiela Pera, Bob Kuntz, and Bud Anderson. It's wonderful to share the enjoyment and enthusiasm for dragonflies and damselflies with all of them, and their questions and comments have helped to sharpen my understanding over the years. I look forward to many more such events in the future.

OdonataCentral and the Dragonfly Society of the Americas have also been very helpful in the production of this book. In particular, the information they have collected from dragonfly observers across the country formed the basis for the Range Maps and Flight Season charts.

The staff at Cave Art Press have been enthusiastic and supportive of this project from the beginning. I would especially like to thank Lisa Wright, who got the ball rolling, and who has done an excellent job of putting all the information and photos together in book form. Her tireless and efficient efforts have made everything run very smoothly. I would also like to thank Arlene Cook for her insightful and meticulous editing, and for many helpful suggestions.

Most of the photos in this guide were taken by me at various dragonfly locations along the Pacific Coast. I also received generous donations of photos from Ray Bruun, Pierre Deviche, Cary Kerst, Dennis Paulson, and Netta Smith. I thank all of them.

Finally, I would like to thank Sabine Deviche (http://devichedesigns.com) for the wonderful artwork in the book. She is a talented and gifted artist, and a pleasure to work with. Her illustrations have added a uniquely artistic, but at the same time scientific, look and feel to the book.

Index

Perched in the bushes,
Smiling up at me,
The Happy-face Dragonfly.

—James S. Walker